ESSENTIALS OF FIRE FIGHTING

COURSE WORKBOOK

Lead Instructional Developer

Elkie Burnside

Instructional Developers

Beth Ann Fulgenzi

Andrea Haken

Lynn Hughes

Melissa Noakes

Lori Raborg

Validated by the International Fire Service Training Association

Published by
Fire Protection Publications
Oklahoma State University

RECYCLABLE

The International Fire Service Training Association (IFSTA) was established in 1934 as a *nonprofit educational association of fire fighting personnel who are dedicated to upgrading fire fighting techniques and safety through training.* To carry out the mission of IFSTA, Fire Protection Publications was established as an entity of Oklahoma State University. Fire Protection Publications' primary function is to publish and distribute training materials as proposed, developed, and validated by IFSTA. As a secondary function, Fire Protection Publications researches, acquires, produces, and markets high-quality learning and teaching aids consistent with IFSTA's mission.

IFSTA holds two meetings each year: the Winter Meeting in January and the Annual Validation Conference in July. During these meetings, committees of technical experts review draft materials and ensure that the professional qualifications of the National Fire Protection Association® standards are met. These Conferences bring together individuals from several related and allied fields, such as:

- Key fire department executives, training officers, and personnel
- Educators from colleges and universities
- Representatives from governmental agencies
- Delegates of firefighter associations and industrial organizations

Committee members are not paid nor are they reimbursed for their expenses by IFSTA or Fire Protection Publications. They participate because of a commitment to the fire service and its future through training. Being on a committee is prestigious in the fire service community, and committee members are acknowledged leaders in their fields. This unique feature provides a close relationship between IFSTA and the fire service community.

IFSTA manuals have been adopted as the official teaching texts of many states and provinces of North America as well as numerous U.S. and Canadian government agencies. Besides the NFPA® requirements, IFSTA manuals are also written to meet the Fire and Emergency Services Higher Education (FESHE) course requirements. A number of the manuals have been translated into other languages to provide training for fire and emergency service personnel in Canada, Mexico, and outside of North America.

ISBN 978-0-87939-512-4

Sixth Edition, First Printing, January 2013 *Printed in the United States of America*

10 9 8 7 6

If you need additional information concerning the International Fire Service Training Association (IFSTA) or Fire Protection Publications, contact:

Customer Service, Fire Protection Publications, Oklahoma State University
930 North Willis, Stillwater, OK 74078-8045
800-654-4055 Fax: 405-744-8204

For assistance with curriculum materials or to ask questions or comment on curriculum content, contact:

Curriculum Department, Fire Protection Publications, Oklahoma State University
930 North Willis, Stillwater, OK 74078-8045
405-744-4111 Fax: 405-744-4112 E-mail: editors@osufpp.org

Table of Contents

Firefighter I

Table of Contents

Firefighter II

Gratitude is extended to the following members of the Fire Protection Publications staff whose contributions made the final publication of this course workbook possible.

Essentials of Fire Fighting, 6th Edition, Curriculum Team

Lead Instructional Developer
Elkie Burnside, Curriculum Technology Manager

Director of Fire Protection Publications
Craig Hannan

FPP Editorial Projects Coordinator
Clint Clausing

Curriculum Technology Manager
Elkie Burnside

Production Coordinator
Ann Moffat

Curriculum Staff
Beth Ann Fulgenzi, Instructional Developer
Andrea Haken, Instructional Developer
Lynn Hughes, Instructional Developer
Brad McLelland, Instructional Developer
Melissa Noakes, Instructional Developer
Lori Raborg, Instructional Developer
David Schaap, Graduate Research Technician

Editorial Staff
Frederick Stowell, Senior Editor
Lynne Murnane, Senior Editor
Gabriel Ramirez, Research Technician
Jake Zlomie, Research Technician
Tara Gladden, Editorial Assistant

Illustrators and Layout Designer
Missy Hannan, Senior Graphics Designer

Technical Reviewers
Steven Dunham
Instructor
Fire Service Training
Oklahoma State University
Stillwater, Oklahoma

Steven Martin
Deputy Director
Delaware State Fire School
Dover, Delaware

How to Use this Workbook

The **Essentials of Firefighting Course Workbook** accompanies the sixth edition of the IFSTA **Essentials of Fire Fighting** as well as the IFSTA/Brady **Essentials of Fire Fighting and Fire Department Operations**.

The workbook is designed to work in a number of ways. The workbook can be used as homework assignments given by your instructor either before a class starts or during class time. The workbook can also be used for self-study. Although the answers are not included in the workbook, page numbers are included that reference manual pages on which the answer can be found.

In either case, the best approach to using this workbook is to read the questions all the way through and answer on your own those that you can. Then go back to the manual and look up those questions that you cannot answer.

The questions in this workbook are divided into Firefighter I and Firefighter II. This division is indicated by color tabs. Firefighter I information is indicated by yellow tabs and Firefighter II information is indicated by red tabs.

The answers to the questions in this workbook can be found in the **Essentials of Firefighting, 6th Edition** Curriculum. If portions of this workbook are assigned as homework, your instructor will have access to these answers.

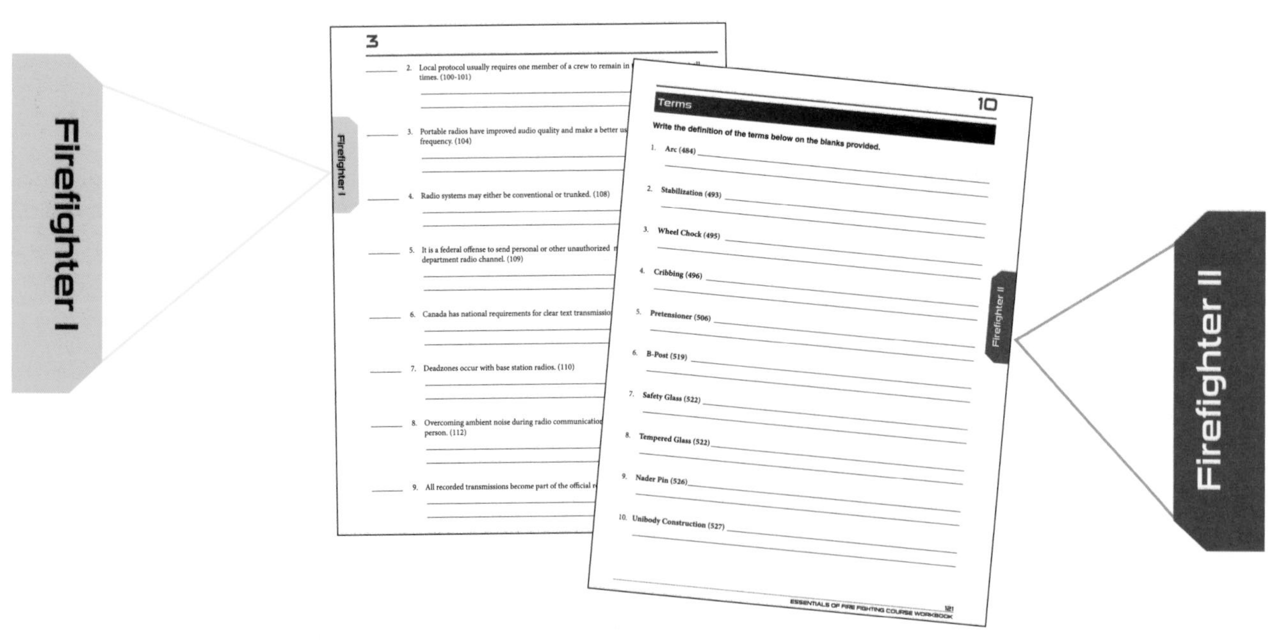

Chapter 1

Orientation and Fire Service History

Terms

Write the definition of the terms below on the blanks provided.

1. **Fireproof (12)** ______________________________

2. **Panic Hardware (12)** ______________________________

3. **Interoperability (14)** ______________________________

4. **Culture (17)** ______________________________

5. **Jargon (18)** ______________________________

6. **Authority Having Jurisdiction (AHJ) (20)** ______________________________

7. **All-Hazard Concept (21)** ______________________________

8. **Line Functions (24)** ______________________________

9. **Staff/Support Functions (24)** ______________________________

10. **External Customers (24)** ______________________________

11. **Internal Customers (24)** ______________________________

12. **Wildland/Urban Interface (26)** ______________________________

13. **Incident Command System (ICS) (28)** ______________________________

14. **Policy (35)** ______________________________

15. **Procedure (36)** ______________________________

16. **Standard Operating Procedure (SOP) (36)** ______________________________

17. **Standard (36)** ______________________________

18. **Code (36)** ______________________________

True/False

Write True or False on the blanks provided; if False, write the correct statement on the lines provided.

_______ 1. The first paid fire company was formed in Boston in 1678. (11)

_______ 2. The use of steel in construction eliminated the potential for disastrous fires. (11)

_______ 3. The National Fire Protection Association® was formed in 1896 to determine how to reduce fire loss in America. (12)

_______ 4. Historical catastrophic fires have lead to the development of modern day safety measures. (12)

_______ 5. The authority having jurisdiction (AHJ) will determine the type and level of service needed to protect citizens in a jurisdiction. (20)

_______ 6. Staff personnel deliver emergency services directly to external customers. (24)

_______ 7. It is the department's responsibility to make sure you learn department regulations. (35)

_______ 8. Orders and directives are used to implement departmental policies and procedures. (36)

_______ 9. Law enforcement agencies may handle fire cause determination in some cases. (38)

_______ 10. The public works department may be responsible for the water distribution system in some jurisdictions. (39)

Matching

Write the correct answers on the blanks provided.

Cultural Strengths

Match the description with the cultural strength listed. Each choice will be used once.

_______ 1. Which cultural strength means valuing the virtues of hard work and thoroughness? (20)

_______ 2. Which cultural strength is displayed by an attitude of admiration toward their peers and superiors? (20)

_______ 3. Which cultural strength is defined as the ability to confront fear, pain, danger, or uncertainty in the course of your profession? (20)

_______ 4. Which cultural strength means firefighters care about the citizens they serve? (20)

_______ 5. Which cultural strength is defined as right or just behavior, with an emphasis on trust? (19)

_______ 6. Which cultural strength is displayed by a defending the department if others try to tarnish its image? (20)

_______ 7. Which cultural strength means doing the right simply because it is right? (19)

_______ 8. Which cultural strength is shown by having a feeling of self-respect and personal worth? (20)

A. Integrity
B. Moral character
C. Work ethic
D. Pride
E. Courage
F. Loyalty
G. Respect
H. Compassion

Fire Companies

Match the question with the type of company listed. Each choice will be used once.

_____ 1. Which type of company performs fire suppression activities involving aircraft accidents? (26)

_____ 2. Which type of company performs technical rescues, including rapid intervention for firefighters? (26)

_____ 3. Which type of company protects structures in the wildland/urban interface? (26)

_____ 4. Which type of company may provide transportation to a medical facility? (26)

_____ 5. Which type of company performs fire suppression duties at structure, vehicle, wildland, and other types of fires? (26)

_____ 6. Which type of company searches for and removes victims from areas of danger or entrapment? (26)

_____ 7. Which type of company mitigates hazardous materials incidents? (26)

_____ 8. Which type of company provides access to upper levels of a structure? (26)

A. Engine company

B. Truck (Ladder) company

C. Rescue squad/company

D. Brush company

E. Hazardous materials company

F. Emergency medical/ ambulance company

G. Special rescue company

H. Aircraft rescue and fire fighting company

Multiple Choice

Write the correct answers on the blanks provided.

_____ 1. The first fire society in Philadelphia was formed by citizens in: (11)

A. 1631.

B. 1647.

C. 1735.

D. 1737.

_____ 2. Which of the following historic fires resulted in mandated fire evacuation drills in schools throughout the academic year? (13)

A. Iroquois Theater Fire, Chicago

B. The Great Fire of 1904, Toronto, Ontario

C. Our Lady of the Angels School Fire, Chicago

D. Ringling Brothers and Barnum and Bailey Circus Fire, Hartford, Connecticut

_____ 3. Which of the following fire service cultural strengths requires promptness, reliability, and initiative? (20)

A. Integrity

B. Courage

C. Work ethic

D. Moral character

_____ 4. Typical organizational structure in the fire service resembles a _____ with the chief at the top and firefighters forming the base. (22)

A. circle

B. square

C. pyramid

D. rhombus

_____ 5. Which of the following types of companies searches for and removes victims from areas of danger? (26)

A. Brush company

B. Engine company

C. Rescue squad/company

D. Hazardous materials company

_____ 6. Which of the following officers manages a variety of functions including emergency operations and administration? (30)

A. Fire marshal

B. Company officer

C. District/battalion chief

D. Assistant/deputy chief

_____ 7. Which of the following officers manages the fire prevention, plan review, and investigation division? (30)

A. Fire marshal

B. Company officer

C. District/battalion chief

D. Assistant/deputy chief

_____ 8. Which of the following fire prevention positions approves architectural and fire protection systems plans for new construction? (31)

A. Plans examiner

B. Fire and arson investigator

C. Fire prevention officer/inspector

D. Public fire and life safety educator

_____ 9. Which of the following fire prevention positions investigates fires and explosions to determine the origin and cause? (31)

A. Plans examiner
B. Fire and arson investigator
C. Fire prevention officer/inspector
D. Public fire and life safety educator

_____ 10. Which of the following is a detailed plan of action for some specific, recurring situation? (36)

A. Code
B. Policy
C. Directive
D. Procedure

_____ 11. Which of the following helps all members of an organization perform to a measureable standard? (36)

A. Policy
B. Code and standard
C. Order and directive
D. Standard operating procedure

Short Answer

Write the correct answers on the blanks provided.

1. What is the basic difference between public and private fire and emergency services organizations? (23)

____

____

____

____

____

2. Describe how the duties of a Firefighter I compare to those of a Firefighter II. (27-28)

____

____

____

____

____

____

3. What are the four levels for Emergency Medical Services Personnel that may be a part of the fire department's service to a community? (30)

4. What are the five organizational characteristics of the fire service? (33)

Crossword Puzzle

Across

4. A set of principles, protocols, or procedures that explain how to do something or provide a set of minimum standards to be followed
7. Provides a coordinated approach to a wide variety of incidents; all responders use a similar, coordinated approach with a common set of authorities, protections, and resources
10. Step-by-step written plan that is closely related to a policy
11. The shared assumptions, beliefs, and values of a group or organization
12. Citizens of the service area protected by the organization
14. Obsolete term for resistance to fire; inappropriate because all materials with the exception of water will burn at some point
15. Ability of two or more systems or components to exchange information and use the information that has been exchanged
16. Guide to decision making in an organization
17. Personnel who provide emergency services to external customers

Down

1. A collection of rules and regulations that has been enacted by law in a particular jurisdiction
2. Employees and membership of the organization
3. Personnel who provide administrative and logistical support to line units
5. Term used in codes and standards to identify the legal entity, such as a building or fire official, that has the statutory authority to enforce a code and to approve or require equipment
6. Hardware mounted on exit doors in public buildings that unlock from the inside and enable doors to be opened when pressure is applied to the release mechanism
8. Line, area, or zone where an undeveloped wildland area meets a human development area
9. Standardized approach to incident management that facilitates interaction between cooperating agencies
13. The specialized or technical language of a trade, profession, or similar group

1
2
3
4
5
6
7
8
9
10
11
12
13
14
15
16
17

Chapter 2

Firefighter Safety and Health

Terms

Write the definition of the terms below on the blanks provided.

1. **Acute (49)** ______________________________

____

2. **Chronic (49)** ______________________________

____

3. **Hazard (50)** ______________________________

____

4. **Mitigate (50)** ______________________________

____

5. **Immediately Dangerous to Life and Health (IDLH) (50)** ______________________________

____

6. **Stressor (52)** ______________________________

____

7. **Employee Assistance Program (EAP) (54)** ______________________________

____

8. **Risk Management Plan (57)** ______________________________

____

9. **Rehabilitation (Rehab) (57)** ______________________________

____

10. **Standard of Care (61)** ______________________________

____

11. **Situational Awareness (67)** ____________________

____

12. **Baffle (71)** ____________________

____

13. **Training Evolution (77)** ____________________

____

14. **Crowd Control (83)** ____________________

____

15. **Collapse Zone (84)** ____________________

____

True/False

Write True or False on the blanks provided; if False, write the correct statement on the lines provided.

_______ 1. Being trapped in a structure fire is the leading cause of firefighter fatalities. (46)

____

____

_______ 2. Acute and chronic are the two main classifications for illnesses. (49)

____

____

_______ 3. It is not possible to prevent respiratory diseases as a firefighter. (50)

____

____

_______ 4. Prescription drugs will not impair a firefighter's ability to operate equipment safely. (51)

____

____

_______ 5. Member assistance and wellness programs focus on job performance only. (59)

_______ 6. Supervisors are given access to information gathered by the employee assistance program. (65)

_______ 7. There are some hazards a driver/operator cannot control while responding to an emergency scene. (66)

_______ 8. A firefighter is never allowed to stand on a moving apparatus. (72)

_______ 9 Preventative maintenance, like keeping aisles unobstructed, can help prevent injuries at fire stations. (74)

_______ 10. Personnel must be fully clothed for any activity that simulates emergency scene conditions. (77)

_______ 11. Firefighter safety at an emergency incident depends on maintaining situational awareness. (80)

_______ 12. A firefighter will never need to perform crowd control. (83)

________ 13. Personnel accountability systems assist in keeping track of firefighters to save lives and prevent injuries. (85)

____

____

Matching

Write the correct answers on the blanks provided.

Costs of Injuries

Match the possible injury cost listed with the correct person or type of department. There is one choice that will not be used.

________ 1. Who pays for possible worker's compensation, but does not need to replace off duty personnel? (48)

________ 2. Who needs to replace off duty personnel, as well as pay for possible worker's compensation? (48)

________ 3. Who suffers physical pain and emotional stress? (48)

A. Individual firefighter
B. Career department
C. Volunteer department
D. Individual firefighter's co-workers

Principles of Braking and Stopping

Match the principle description with the correct term. There is one choice that will not be used.

________ 1. What is the distance the apparatus travels from when the driver/operator realizes the need to stop and until the driver/operator's foot touches the brake pedal? (70)

________ 2. What is the sum of driver-reaction distance and braking distance? (70)

________ 3. What is the distance the apparatus travels from when the driver/operator touches the brake pedal until vehicle is completely stopped? (70)

A. Braking distance
B. Driver-reaction distance
C. Total stopping distance
D. Total reaction distance

Personnel Accountability Systems

Match the personnel accountability system description with the correct term. There is one choice that will not be used.

_____ 1. What is the system that uses radio-based tracking attached to PPE called? (86)

_____ 2. What is the system that uses passports attached to a control board called? (86)

_____ 3. What is the system that uses information maintained by an Accountability Officer to track entry and expected exit times called? (86)

A. Passport system

B. SCBA tag system

C. Computer-based electronic accountability systems

D. One-to-one tracking system

Multiple Choice

Write the correct answers on the blanks provided.

_____ 1. Which of the following can be the result of physical and emotional stress built over time while responding to emergency incidents? (52)

A. Obesity

B. Headaches

C. Lung cancer

D. Stress-induced hypertension

_____ 2. Which of the following is NOT the department's responsibility in preventing tobacco dependence? (54)

A. Do not start tobacco use

B. Provide tobacco cessation programs

C. Prohibit smoking in department facilities

D. Require probationary firefighters do not smoke

_____ 3. Which of the following NFPA® standards outlines safety and health program related policies? (56)

A. NFPA® 1403

B. NFPA® 1500

C. NFPA® 1582

D. NFPA® 1851

_____ 4. What nonemergency issue must a safety and health program address? (56)
   A. Alcohol abuse
   B. Firefighting hazards
   C. Communicable diseases
   D. Driving apparatus hazards

_____ 5. Emergency operations are limited to: (57)
   A. those that will save the most property.
   B. those that are safe for personnel on scene.
   C. those that can be completed within 24 hours.
   D. those that can be safely conducted by personnel on scene.

_____ 6. Which of the following is the goal of a critical incident stress management program? (59)
   A. To help firefighters with daily stress
   B. To assist members who are in Command
   C. To assist members involved in highly stressful events
   D. To help firefighters with personal issues that may impact job performance

_____ 7. ______ regulations are designed to ensure workplaces are free from hazards that can cause death or serious injury. (60)
   A. OSHA
   B. NFPA®
   C. ProQual
   D. State/Province

_____ 8. Which program works to prevent human suffering as well as damage to equipment? (63)
   A. Member assistance program
   B. Safety and health program
   C. Safety stand-down program
   D. Everyone goes home program

_____ 9. Firefighters can BEST maintain personal health by which of the following? (64)
   A. Volunteering for extra shifts
   B. Adopting a healthy lifestyle
   C. Living a completely stress-free life
   D. Participating in continuing education

_____ 10. Which of the following is the BEST way to help avoid and combat skids? (72)

A. Always use turn signals
B. Use hearing protection when needed
C. Test brakes at low speed on slick roads
D. Drive the same no matter what the conditions

_____ 11. What type of tools should be used in potentially flammable atmospheres? (76)

A. Power saws
B. Power tools
C. Power drills
D. Intrinsically safe tools

_____ 12. Which of the following needs to be disinfected after live fire training? (78)

A. Power tools
B. Fire apparatus
C. CPR manikins
D. Unpowered tools

_____ 13. What part of firefighter safety requires regular inspection of tools and restocking of supplies? (79)

A. Preparedness
B. Roadway incident safety
C. Emergency scene safety
D. National Incident Management System

_____ 14. What type of zone takes into account type of construction, other exposures, and the safest location for apparatus and personnel? (84-85)

A. Hot zone
B. Cold zone
C. Control zone
D. Collapse zone

Short Answer

Write the correct answers on the blanks provided.

1. Describe the steps firefighters can take to prevent exposure-related diseases. (54)

____

____

____

____

2. Explain the basic concept that supports risk management. (62)

____

____

____

____

____

3. Describe how firefighters can maintain situational awareness at roadway incidents. (80)

____

____

____

____

Crossword Puzzle

Across

4. Allowing firefighters to rest, rehydrate, and recover during an incident

6. Level of care that all persons should receive; care that does not meet this standard is considered inadequate

9. Area beneath a wall in which the wall is likely to land if it loses structural integrity

12. Program to help employees and their families with work or personal problems

13. Limiting the access of non-emergency personnel to the emergency scene

Down

1. To make less harsh or intense; to alleviate

2. Condition, substance, or device that can directly cause injury or loss; the source of a risk

3. Intermediate partial bulkhead that reduces the surge effect in a partially loaded liquid tank

5. Operation of fire and emergency services training covering one or several aspects of fire fighting

6. Perception of the surrounding environment, and the ability to anticipate future events

7. Sharp or severe; having a rapid onset and short duration

8. Written plan that analyzes the exposure to hazards, implements appropriate risk management techniques, and establishes criteria for monitoring their effectiveness

10. Long-term and reoccurring

11. Any agent, condition, or experience that causes stress

1
2
3
4
5
6
7
8
9
10
11
12
13

Chapter 3

Fire Department Communications

Firefighter I

Terms

Write the definition of the terms below on the lines provided.

1. **Public Safety Answering Point (PSAP) (96)** ______

2. **Automatic Location Identification (ALI) (98)** ______

3. **Global Positioning System (GPS) (98)** ______

4. **Base Station Radios (104)** ______

5. **Intrinsically Safe Equipment (104)** ______

6. **Clear Text (109)** ______

True/False

Write True or False on the blanks provided; if False, write the correct statement on the lines provided.

______ 1. Firefighters must be able to obtain the same information as a telecommunicator. (98)

______

_______ 2. Local protocol usually requires one member of a crew to remain in the watch room at all times. (100-101)

____

____

_______ 3. Portable radios have improved audio quality and make a better use of their assigned frequency. (104)

____

____

_______ 4. Radio systems may either be conventional or trunked. (108)

____

____

_______ 5. It is a federal offense to send personal or other unauthorized messages over a designated fire department radio channel. (109)

____

____

_______ 6. Canada has national requirements for clear text transmissions. (109)

____

____

_______ 7. Deadzones occur with base station radios. (110)

____

____

_______ 8. Overcoming ambient noise during radio communication is the responsibility of each person. (112)

____

____

_______ 9. All recorded transmissions become part of the official record on the incident. (112)

____

____

_______ 10. Units or individuals must identify themselves in every transmission as outlined in the local radio protocol. (112)

____

____

Multiple Choice

Write the correct answers on the blanks provided.

_____ 1. Which of the following would be information gathered by a dispatcher? (98)

A. The caller's callback number
B. The names of the people involved
C. The caller's relation to the emergency
D. The weather conditions at the incident

_____ 2. Which of the following is NOT a type of public alerting system? (98-99)

A. Radio fire alarm
B. Telephone fire alarm
C. Wired telegraph circuit
D. Two-way radio system

_____ 3. Which of the following is an example of dispatching emergency services? (101)

A. Posting a message
B. Answering the telephone
C. Sounding sirens in a small community
D. Reporting number of calls about an incident to fire crew

_____ 4. Portable radios are: (104)

A. simplex systems.
B. dispatch devices.
C. handheld devices.
D. computer-based systems.

_____ 5. Which of the following is the straight line of travel of radio signals between an antenna connected to a transmitter and an antenna connected to a receiver? (106)

A. Direct communication
B. External communication
C. Internal communication
D. Half-duplex communication

_____ 6. Which of the following allows radio communication in both directions simultaneously? (106)
   A. Direct system
   B. Simplex system
   C. Full-duplex system
   D. Half-duplex system

_____ 7. What happens if the talkgroup is not available? (106)
   A. A failure tone sounds.
   B. The system shuts down.
   C. A two-way radio must be used.
   D. The radio forces you to wait a few seconds and try again.

_____ 8. Which of the following permits one radio to call another much like a telephone call? (109)
   A. Clear text
   B. Private call
   C. Multigroup call
   D. Dynamic regrouping

_____ 9. Departments using the National Incident Management System (NIMS) discontinued the use of: (109)
   A. ten-codes.
   B. clear text.
   C. talkgroup.
   D. multigroup call.

_____ 10. Using your body or PPE to create a wind barrier when transmitting can eliminate: (112)
   A. ambient noises.
   B. failure tone sounds.
   C. additional resources.
   D. shut down of systems.

Short Answer

Write the correct answers on the lines provided.

1. What instant information from Enhanced 9-1-1 is provided to a dispatcher? (98)

2. List the responsibilities for monitoring a watch room. (101)

3. What are three possible ways to overcome physical barriers when using a portable radio? (110)

4. List the best practices of radio communication. (114-115)

Crossword

Across

3. Equipment designed and approved for use in flammable atmospheres that is incapable of releasing sufficient electrical energy to cause the ignition of a flammable atmospheric mixture
4. Use of plain language, including certain standard words and phrases, in radio communications transmissions
5. System for determining position on the earth's surface by calculating the difference in time for the signal from a number of satellites to reach a receiver on the ground

Down

1. Any location or facility at which 9-1-1 calls are answered either by direct calling, rerouting, or diversion
2. Fixed, nonmobile radio at a central location

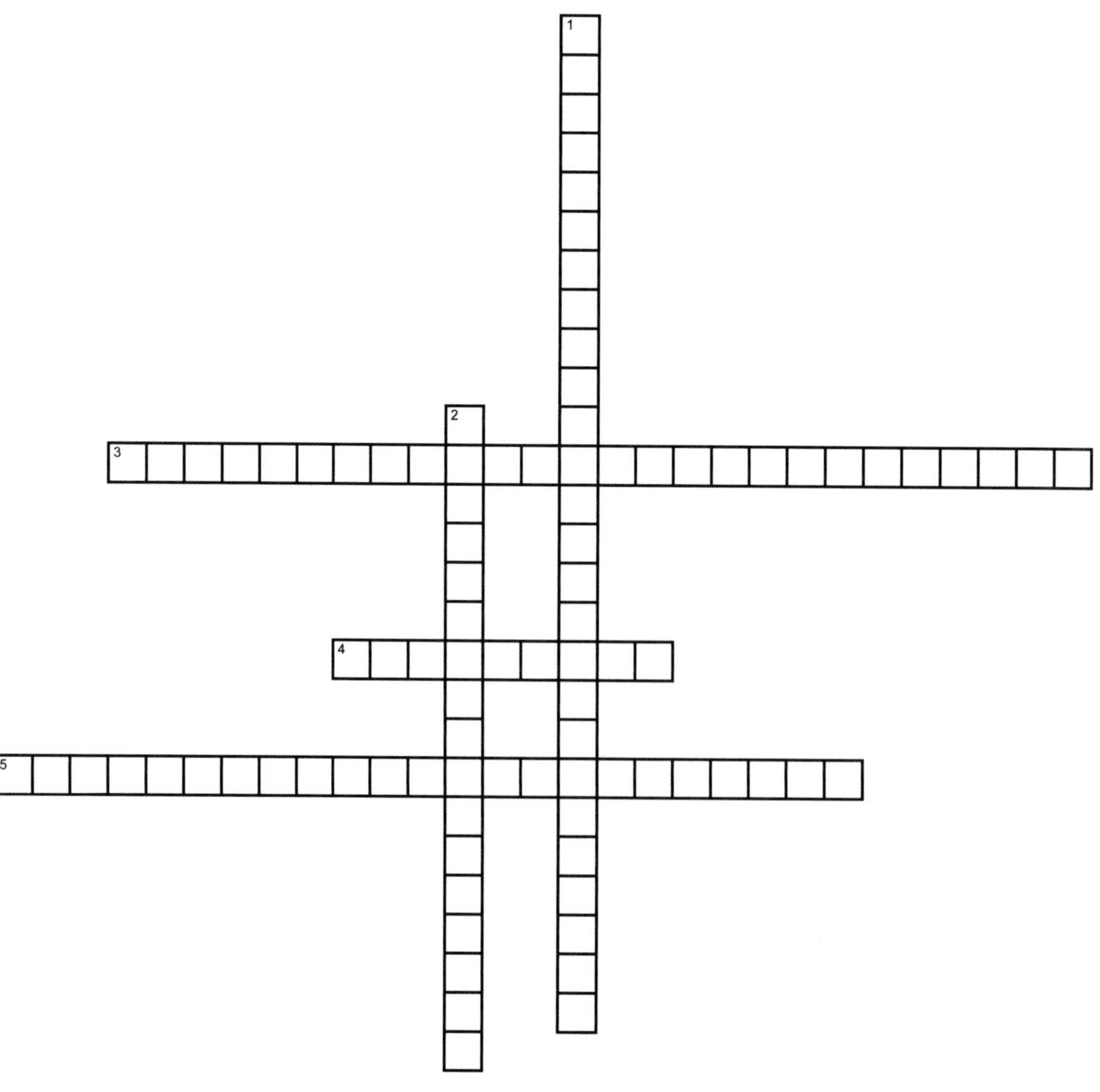

Terms

Write the definition of the terms below on the blanks provided.

1. **Alarm Assignment (119)** ____

____

2. **Personnel Accountability Report (PAR) (120)** ____

____

3. **National Fire Incident Reporting System (NFIRS) (122)** ____

____

True/False

Write True or False on the blanks provided; if False, write the correct statement on the lines provided.

________ 1. If first on-scene you should provide the postincident report. (116)

____

____

________ 2. A radio-equipped, mobile communications vehicle can be used at large incidents to maintain communication. (119)

____

____

________ 3. Each supervisor must verify the status of those under command and report it. (120)

____

____

________ 4. Postincident reports can be handwritten. (121-122)

____

____

3

Fill in the Blank

Write the correct answer on the blanks provided.

1. The two basic arrival situations are ________________ and ________________of an emergency. (117)

2. Emergency radio traffic begins with a clear statement such as __________________________. (119)

3. The unit originating emergency radio traffic states the type of hazard and action required, such as ________________________________. (119)

Multiple Choice

Write the correct answers on the blanks provided.

_____ 1. The address of incident, operational strategy, and routing instructions are all provided in which report? (116-117)
   - A. Arrival
   - B. Progress
   - C. Postincident
   - D. Personal accountability

_____ 2. Which of the following contains transfer of command, direction of fire spread, and anticipated actions? (117-118)
   - A. Arrival report
   - B. Progress report
   - C. Postincident report
   - D. Personal accountability report

_____ 3. Which of the following provides a report that includes air consumption to the Incident Commander (IC)? (118-119)
   - A. Initial radio report
   - B. Tactical progress report
   - C. Personal accountability report
   - D. Request for additional resource

_____ 4. What organization developed the National Fire Incident Reporting System (NFIRS)? (122)
   - A. United States Fire Administration (USFA)
   - B. Federal Communications Commission (FCC)
   - C. National Fire Protection Association (NFPA®)
   - D. Emergency Service Specific Telecommunications Center

_____ 5. How the emergency was reported, the type of call, and the actions taken are general information included in the: (122)

A. arrival report.

B. progress report.

C. postincident report.

D. personal accountability report.

Short Answer

Write the correct answers on the lines provided.

1. List the parts of an initial report. (116-117)

____

____

____

____

2. Provide the reasons information is gathered for a postincident report. (122)

____

____

____

____

____

____

____

____

Chapter 4

Building Construction

Terms

Write the definition of the terms below on the blanks provided.

1. **Green Wood (135)** ______________________________

____

2. **Oriented Strand Board (OSB) (135)** ______________________________

____

3. **Masonry (135)**______________________________

____

4. **Veneer Walls (135)** ______________________________

____

5. **Spalling (135)** ______________________________

____

6. **Lightweight Steel Truss (137)**______________________________

____

7. **Curtain Wall (137)** ______________________________

____

8. **Rebar (138)** ______________________________

____

9. **Hybrid Construction (141)** ______________________________

____

10. **Protected Steel (144)** ______________________________

11. **Fire-Resistance Rating (145)** ______________________________

12. **Fire Stop (145)** ______________________________

13. **Load-Bearing Wall (147)** ______________________________

14. **Stud (148)** ______________________________

15. **Non-Load-Bearing Wall (160)** ______________________________

16. **Partition Wall (160)** ______________________________

17. **Fire Wall (160)** ______________________________

18. **Party Wall (160)** ______________________________

19. **Parapet (162)** ______________________________

20. **Ridge (162)** ______________________________

21. **Eave (163)** ______________________________

22. **Rafter (165)** ______________________________

____

23. **Parallel Chord Truss (165)** ______________________________

____

24. **Joists (166)** ______________________________

____

25. **Lightweight Wood Truss (166)** ______________________________

____

26. **Gusset Plates (165)** ______________________________

____

27. **Purlin (166)** ______________________________

____

28. **Cockloft (170)** ______________________________

____

29. **Dead Load (170)** ______________________________

____

30. **Rain Roof (172)** ______________________________

____

31. **Live Load (174)** ______________________________

____

32. **Means of Egress (174)** ______________________________

____

True/False

Write True or False on the blanks provided; if False, write the correct statement on the lines provided.

_______ 1. Masonry is the most common building material in North America. (134)

_______ 2. The effect of heat on metal will depend on the type of metal and if it is exposed or covered. (135)

_______ 3. Wrought iron is the primary material used in the construction of large modern buildings. (137)

_______ 4. Manufactured structures are required to conform to model building codes. (149)

_______ 5. Wall rated assemblies may be continuous from one floor to the bottom of the next floor. (160)

_______ 6. There is always an external sign, like a soft roof, before roof collapse. (166)

_______ 7. Roof penetrations and openings can allow firefighters to gain access to attics. (170)

______ 8. When off, solar panels retain no electricity. (171)

______ 9. Rain roofs may hide heating, ventilation, and air conditioning (HVAC) units that can contribute to collapse potential. (172)

______ 10. Roof mounted equipment is never hidden from plain sight. (174)

______ 11. Smokeproof stair enclosures are required in all buildings. (177)

______ 12. Fire doors must pass a test by a third-party testing agency. (183)

______ 13. Window security may prevent the escape of trapped victims and firefighters in emergency situations. (189)

Identification

Write the correct answers on the blanks provided.

Roof Types (161-163)

Identify the type of roof in the image below.

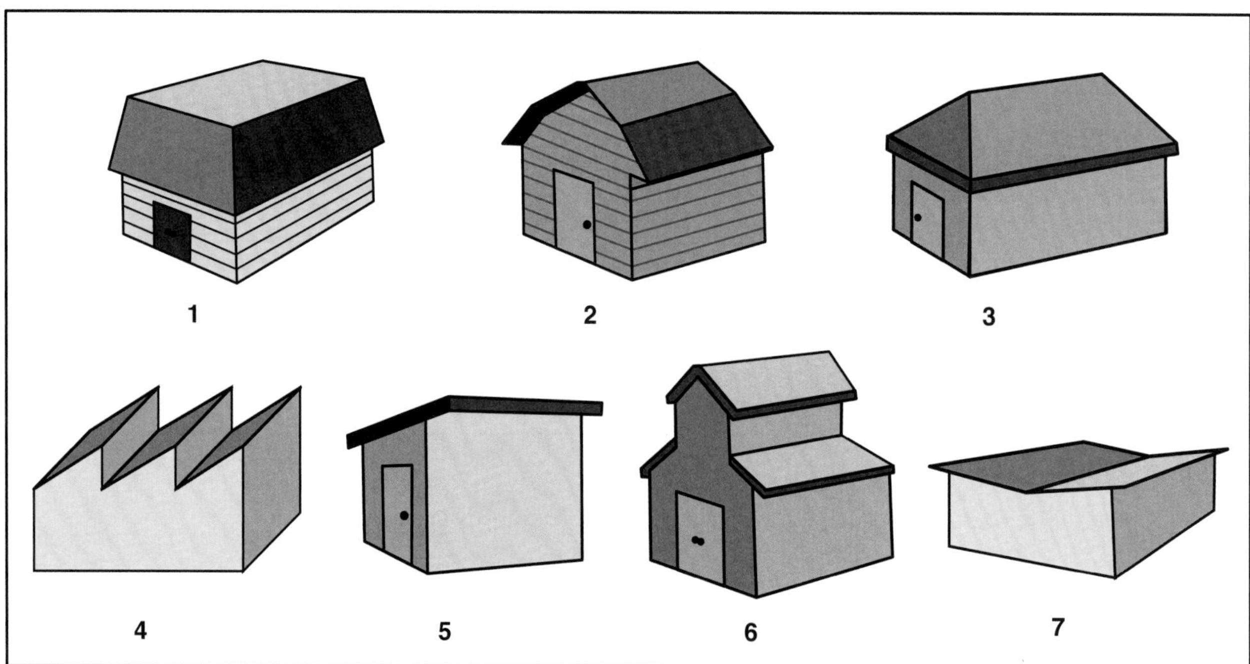

1. ______________________________

2. ______________________________

3. ______________________________

4. ______________________________

5. ______________________________

6. ______________________________

7. ______________________________

Stair Types (174-177)

Identify the type of stairs in the image below.

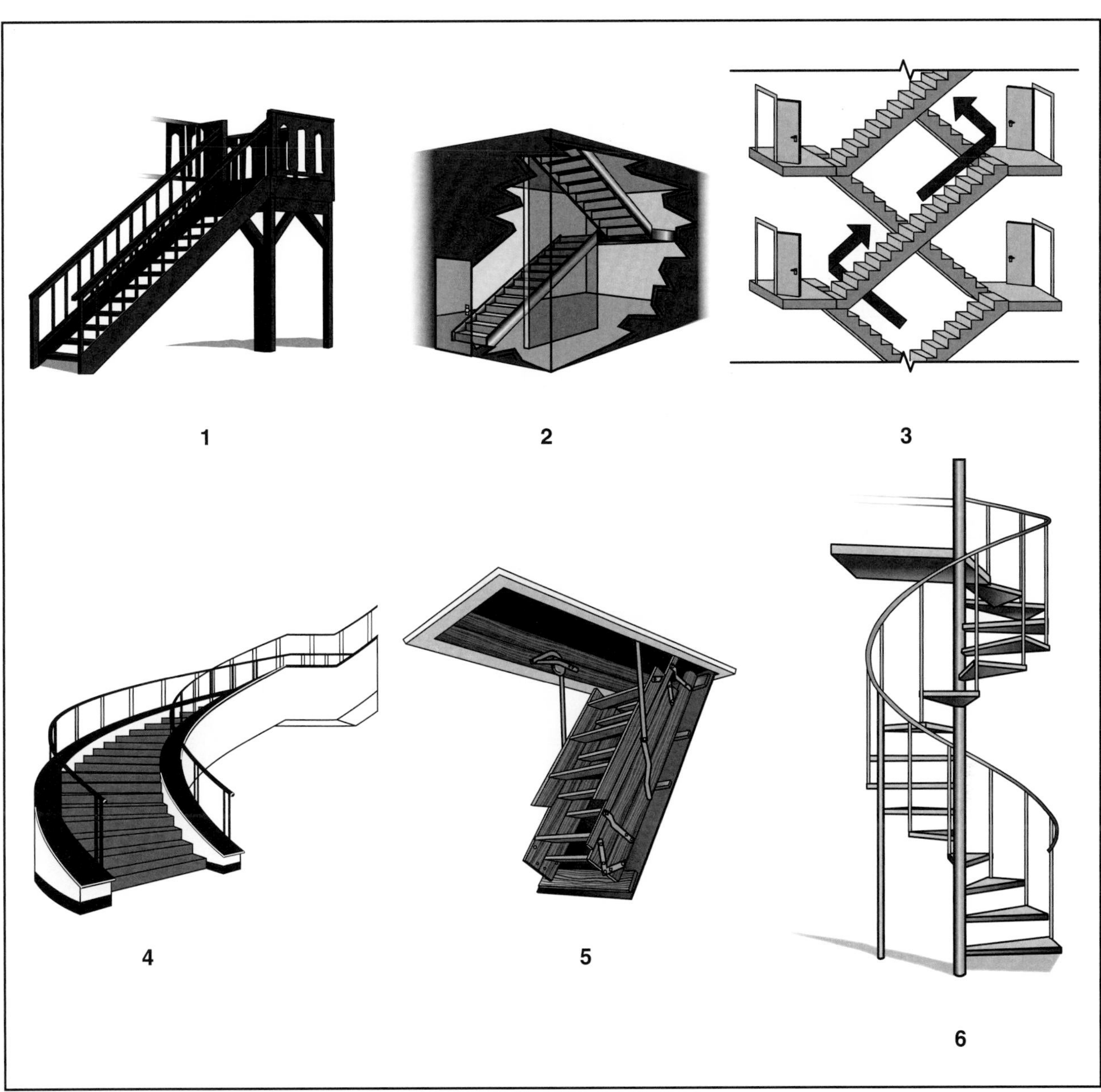

1. ______________________

2. ______________________

3. ______________________

4. ______________________

5. ______________________

6. ______________________

Parts of a Window (186-187)

Identify the parts of the window in the image below.

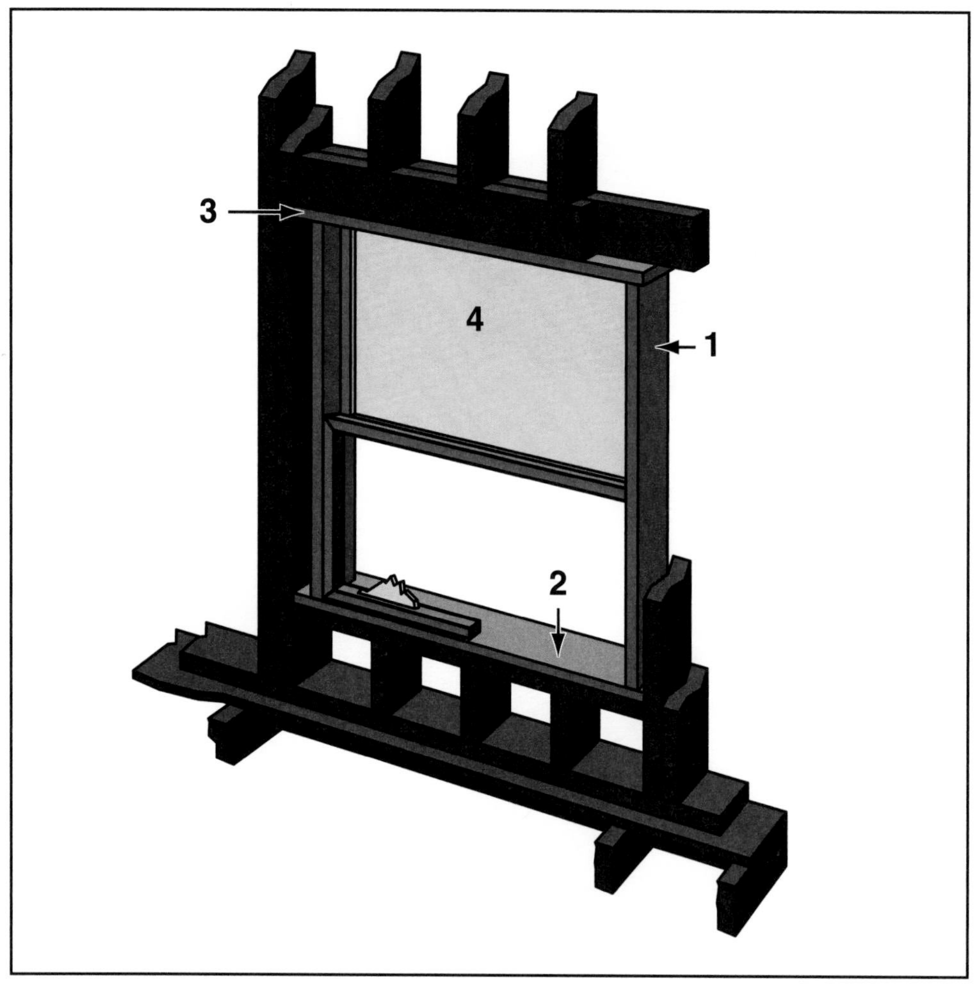

1. ______________________________

2. ______________________________

3. ______________________________

4. ______________________________

Matching

Write the correct answers on the blanks provided.

Common Building Materials

Match the definition with the common building material listed. Each choice will be used once.

________	1. Material also known as drywall or Sheetrock®; this material absorbs heat as moisture evaporates. (139)	A.	Wood
________	2. Building material that includes bricks, stones, and concrete blocks; this material is minimally affected by fire and exposure to high temperatures. (135)	B.	Masonry
________	3. When melted this material can contribute to fire load; this material is used on structure exteriors, for water and sewer pipes, as well as for decorative uses. (141)	C.	Metal
________	4. Building material that is internally fortified with steel reinforcement bars (rebar) or wire mesh; this material performs well under fire conditions but can lose strength through spalling. (138)	D.	Reinforced concrete
________	5. Material that is not typically used for structural support; this material can be found in sheet, block, and wire-reinforced forms. (140)	E.	Gypsum
________	6. Material that is manufactured by combining two or more distinctly different materials; this material is lightweight, has high structural strength and resistance to chemical wear. (141)	F.	Lath and plaster
________	7. The most common building material used in North America; this is the main component in a variety of structural assemblies. (134)	G.	Glass
________	8. A process, not a single material; this material is difficult to penetrate with axes and can conceal fire in the cavity between spaces. (139)	H.	Plastic
________	9. Building material that is used to provide structural support, decorative coverings, and window frames; the effect of heat will depend on if this material is exposed or covered. (135)	I.	Composite materials

Building Components

Match the definition with the building component listed. Each choice will be used once.

_________ 1. Component that defines the perimeter of a building and divides it into compartment or rooms. (160)

_________ 2. Component that can vary widely in operation, style, design, and construction. Classified by the way it operates; includes sliding, folding, vertical, and revolving. (178)

_________ 3. Component that forms the top and bottom of a compartment; its construction varies depending on level. (159)

_________ 4. Component in which construction varies; the two main categories are fixed and movable. (186-187)

_________ 5. Component that provides access to or egress from different levels of a structure. (174)

_________ 6. Component designed to support the weight of the building and all its contents. (158)

_________ 7. Component that functions to protect a structure and its contents from the effects of weather. (161)

A. Foundations
B. Floors/ceilings
C. Walls
D. Roofs
E. Stairs
F. Doors
G. Windows

Roof Obstructions

Match the definition with the roof obstruction listed. Each choice will be used once.

_________ 1. Obstruction that is found in cold and snowy climates to prevent ice damming and icicle formation at the eaves; designed to prevent interior heat from escaping into attic space. (171)

_________ 2. Obstruction that can create a void which conceals the fire and allows it to burn undetected; may also hide HVAC units, adding to collapse potential. (172)

_________ 3. Obstruction that adds a live load to the dead load distributed on a roof; it increases collapse potential and may affect ventilation. (174)

_________ 4. Obstruction that represents a significant hazard; hazards include tripping over panels and the amount of electricity contained by panels even when off. (171)

A. Green roofs
B. Cold roofs
C. Photovoltaic roofs
D. Rain roofs
E. Security
F. Roof-mounted equipment

(Cont.)

_________ 5. Obstruction that can take several forms ranging from a few potted plants and flower boxes to a layer of earth with growing plants covering a large area of the roof. (170)

_________ 6. Obstruction put into place to prevent illegal entry; may be modified by building occupants. (173)

Types of Movable Windows
Match the definition with the type of movable window listed. Each choice will be used once.

_________ 1. Window that has one or more top-hinged, outward-swinging sashes that are opened by unlatching and pushing or by using a mechanical window crank. (189)

_________ 2. Window that has a side-hinged sash that is usually installed to swing outward. (187)

_________ 3. Window that swings outward at the top or bottom and slides upward or downward in grooves. (189)

_________ 4. Window that has two or more sashes, at least one of which moves horizontally within the frame. (189)

_________ 5. Window that has a sash that pivots horizontally or vertically about a central axis. (189)

_________ 6. Window that has two sashes that move past each other in a vertical plane. (187)

_________ 7. Window that has only one sash openable. (187)

_________ 8. Window that has a large number of narrow overlapping glass sections that swing outward. (189)

A. Double-hung
B. Single-hung
C. Casement
D. Horizontal sliding
E. Awning
F. Jalousie
G. Projecting
H. Pivoting

Multiple Choice

Write the correct answers on the blanks provided.

_____ 1. What type of masonry rarely shows any sign of serious deterioration? (135)

A. Stones
B. Bricks
C. Mortar
D. Concrete blocks

_____ 2. Which of the following building materials is not typically used for structural support? (140)

A. Wood

B. Metal

C. Glass/fiberglass

D. Reinforced concrete

_____ 3. Finger-jointed timber, laminated timber, and medium density fiberboard (MDF) are all examples of what type of building material? (142)

A. Glass/fiberglass

B. Lath and plaster

C. Composite materials

D. Reinforced concrete

_____ 4. Canadian construction types are defined by which of the following? (151)

A. *Novoclimat standard*

B. Local jurisdictional building codes

C. National Building Code of Canada (NBC®)

D. National Fire Protection Association® (NFPA®)

_____ 5. What type of wall may be used as party walls to separate two adjacent structures to prevent fire spread? (160)

A. Fire wall

B. Penetrating wall

C. Load-bearing wall

D. Non-load-bearing wall

_____ 6. What part of a roof can act as a support and may be the same as a roof covering? (166)

A. Deck

B. Support

C. Purlin

D. Sheathing

_____ 7. Which of the following BEST describes a nonpermitted structural modification? (173-174)

A. Additions to the structure

B. Removal of roof supports

C. Removal of non-load-bearing walls

D. Replacement of fire escapes with enclosed stairways

_____ 8. What door type has the advantage of eliminating door swing that might interfere with the use of interior space? (179)

A. Sliding doors

B. Vertical doors

C. Folding doors

D. Swinging doors

_____ 9. What type of door is constructed with spacers between face panels to provide lateral support? (182)

A. Panel door

B. Flush door

C. Solid-core door

D. Hollow core door

_____ 10. What type of door has the disadvantage of requiring clear space around the door to ensure closure? (185)

A. Swinging fire doors

B. Rolling steel fire doors

C. All types of fire doors

D. Horizontal sliding fire doors

Short Answer

Write the correct answers on the blanks provided.

1. List the five construction classifications and give a brief description of each. (144-149)

____

____

____

____

____

2. What are the main types of occupancy classifications and how do they differ? (151-152)

____

____

____

Crossword Puzzle

Across

2. Wall, usually interior, that supports only its own weight
5. A non-load- bearing wall, often of glass and steel, fixed to the outside of a building and serving especially as cladding
8. These trusses are used as floor joists in multistory buildings and as ceiling joists in buildings with flat roofs
11. Rating assigned to a material or assembly after standardized testing by an independent testing organization; identifies the amount of time a material or assembly will resist a typical fire, as measured on a standard time-temperature curve
14. Interior non-load-bearing wall that separates a space into rooms
15. Concealed space between the top floor and the roof of a structure
17. Continuous and unobstructed way of exit travel from any point in a building or structure to a public way, consisting of three separate and distinct parts: exit access, exit, and exit discharge
18. Portion of the exterior walls of a building that extends above the roof. A low wall at the edge of a roof

Down

1. Walls with a surface layer of attractive material laid over a base of common material
3. Weight of the structure, structural members, building components, and any other features permanently attached to the building that are constant and immobile
4. A wooden structural panel formed by gluing and compressing wood strands together under pressure. This material has replaced plywood and planking in the majority of construction applications
6. Structural supports constructed of 2- × 3-inch or 2- × 4-inch (50 mm by 75 mm or 50 mm by 100 mm) members that are connected by gusset plates
7. A load-bearing wall shared by two adjacent structures
9. Items within a building that are movable but are not included as a permanent part of the structure; merchandise, stock, furnishings, occupants, firefighters, and the water used for fire suppression are examples of live loads
10. Horizontal member between trusses that support the roof
11. Fire-rated wall with a specified degree of fire resistance, built of fire-resistive materials and usually extending from the foundation up to and through the roof of a building, that is designed to limit the spread of a fire within a structure or between adjacent structures
12. Expansion of excess moisture within masonry materials due to exposure to the heat of a fire, resulting in tensile forces within the material, and causing it to break apart
13. Horizontal structural members used to support a ceiling or floor. Drywall materials are nailed or screwed to the ceiling joists, and the subfloor is nailed or screwed to the floor joists

16. Solid materials, such as wood blocks, used to prevent or limit the vertical and horizontal spread of fire and the products of combustion in hollow walls or floors, above false ceilings, in penetrations for plumbing or electrical installations, in penetrations of a fire-rated assembly, or in cocklofts and crawl spaces

4

Terms

Write the definition of the terms below on the blanks provided.

1. **Structural Collapse (195)** ______________________________

2. **Balloon Frame Construction (201)** ______________________________

3. **Platform Frame Construction (201)** ______________________________

True/False

Write True or False on the blanks provided; if False, write the correct statement on the lines provided.

_______ 1. Arrangement of materials in a building does not directly affect fire development. (191)

_______ 2. The most effective defense against heavy content loading is proper inspection and code enforcement. (192)

_______ 3. Furnishings and finishes do not contribute to fire spread and smoke production. (192)

_______ 4. Unprotected steel and wooden trusses can fail from exposure to heat alone. (193)

_________ 5. Collapse potential is only a concern during the emergency phase of an incident. (195)

_________ 6. The safest place for personnel in defensive operations is the corner of the building. (201)

Matching

Write the correct answers on the blanks provided.

Sizing Up Existing Construction

Match the construction component with the size-up question listed. Each choice will be used once.

_________ 1. Is it flat, pitched, or arched; what type of covering is visible? (190)

_________ 2. Can these be opened from inside; are there grilles that should be removed from outside? (191)

_________ 3. How many, above and below ground, are visible; are there any below ground on one side of the building that are above ground on the other? (190)

_________ 4. Have additions been made that may create internal hazards? (190)

_________ 5. Are there obvious signs of deterioration? (190)

_________ 6. Are there HVAC units, water tanks, or other heavy objects visible? (190)

_________ 7. Is it wood-frame, unreinforced masonry, all-metal, or concrete? (190)

A. Age of the building
B. Construction materials
C. Roof type
D. Renovations and modifications
E. Dead loads
F. Number of stories
G. Windows

Construction Type Collapse Zone Guidelines

Match the construction type with the collapse zone guideline listed. Each choice will be used once.

_____ 1. The collapse zone for this type of construction should be established if a fire is intense or if the structure has been weakened over time by repeated fires. (200)

_____ 2. When debris from this construction type strikes the ground, it can travel or even cause the collapse of other structures. (200)

_____ 3. The primary concern is flying glass; zones must consider direction and velocity that wind currents may carry glass. (199)

_____ 4. It is rare for this type of structure to collapse outward, the greater danger is interior collapse. (200)

_____ 5. Structures of this type will expand and twist, pushing out walls when exposed to temperatures above 1,000° F (537.78° C). (199)

A. Type I
B. Type II
C. Type III
D. Type IV
E. Type V

Multiple Choice

Write the correct answers on the blanks provided.

_____ 1. Even when treated with fire retardant, _____________ can contribute to fire spread. (192)
A. bricks
B. concrete
C. wood shakes
D. lightweight trusses

_____ 2. Estimate the collapse zone by taking the height of the structure and: (199)
A. add 20.
B. subtract 15.
C. divide by a factor of 22.
D. multiply by a factor of 1½.

_____ 3. What part of Type III construction carries the exterior load? (200)
- A. Steel I-beams
- B. Wood frames and veneer
- C. Concrete, brick, or masonry
- D. Wood, masonry, or unprotected steel

_____ 4. Which of the following is a reason to establish a collapse zone? (201)
- A. A defensive strategy has been adopted.
- B. There is no evidence of structural instability.
- C. Masonry mortar shows no sign of deterioration.
- D. Furnishings and finishes do not overwhelm fire suppression systems.

Short Answer

Write the correct answers on the blanks provided.

1. What are at least three things that knowledge of construction types can help firefighters identify? (190)

____

____

____

____

2. What are potential contributors to faster than normal fire growth in renovated, demolished, or abandoned structures? (194)

____

____

____

____

3. What are the main structural collapse factors that must be considered? (195)

4. List at least five indicators of potential or imminent collapse. (198-199)

5. What are the actions to be taken when collapse is imminent? (199)

Chapter 5

Fire Behavior

Firefighter I

Terms

Write the definition of the terms below on the blanks provided.

1. **Combustion (208)** ______________________________

2. **Fire (208)** ______________________________

3. **Heat (208)** ______________________________

4. **Temperature (208)** ______________________________

5. **Fuel (208)** ______________________________

6. **Oxidizer (208)** ______________________________

7. **Matter (208)** ______________________________

8. **Energy (209)** ______________________________

9. **Oxidation (209)** ______________________________

10. **Potential Energy (209)** ______________________________

11. **Kinetic Energy (209)** ______________________________

12. **Joules (J) (210)** ______________________________

13. **Exothermic Reaction (210)** ______________________________

14. **Endothermic Reaction (210)** ______________________________

15. **Pyrolysis (210)** ______________________________

16. **Vaporization (210)** ______________________________

17. **Ignition (210)** ______________________________

18. **Piloted Ignition (210)** ______________________________

19. **Autoignition (210)** ______________________________

20. **Autoignition Temperature (212)** ______________________________

21. **Flame (212)** ______________________________

____

22. **Fire Triangle (212)** ______________________________

____

23. **Fire Tetrahedron (212)** ______________________________

____

24. **Passive Agent (212)** ______________________________

____

25. **Products of Combustion (214)** ______________________________

____

26. **Carbon Monoxide (CO) (215)** ______________________________

____

27. **Hydrogen Cyanide (HCN) (215)** ______________________________

____

28. **Carbon Dioxide (CO_2) (216)** ______________________________

____

29. **Thermal Energy (216)** ______________________________

____

30. **Self-Heating (217)** ______________________________

____

31. **Spontaneous Ignition (217)** ______________________________

____

32. **Heat Flux (219)** ____________________

33. **Conduction (219)** ____________________

34. **Convection (219)** ____________________

35. **Radiation (219)** ____________________

36. **Buoyant (221)** ____________________

37. **Flow Path (222)** ____________________

38. **Upper Layer (223)** ____________________

39. **Reducing Agent (223)** ____________________

40. **Heat of Combustion (223)** ____________________

41. **Heat Release Rate (HRR) (223)** ____________________

42. **Watt (224)** ____________________

43. **Vapor Density (226)** ______________________________

____

44. **Specific Gravity (226)** ______________________________

____

45. **Flammable Liquid (226)** ______________________________

____

46. **Vapor Pressure (226)** ______________________________

____

47. **Flash Point (227)** ______________________________

____

48. **Fire Point (227)** ______________________________

____

49. **Solubility (227)** ______________________________

____

50. **Miscible (227)** ______________________________

____

51. **Hydrocarbon Fuel (227)** ______________________________

____

52. **Polar Solvents (227)** ______________________________

____

53. **Combustible Liquid (228)** ______________________________

____

54. **Flammable Range (232)** ____

____

55. **Upper Flammable (Explosive) Limit (UFL) (232)** ____

____

56. **Lower Flammable (Explosive) Limit (LFL) (232)** ____

____

57. **Free Radicals (233)** ____

____

58. **Chemical Flame Inhibition (234)** ____

____

59. **Fuel Controlled (239)** ____

____

60. **Ventilation Controlled (239)** ____

____

61. **Ambient Conditions (240)** ____

____

62. **Fuel Load (241)** ____

____

63. **Incipient Stage (241)** ____

____

64. **Plume (242)** ____

____

65. **Ceiling Jet (242)** ______________________________

____

66. **Thermal Layering (244)** ______________________________

____

67. **Neutral Plane (244)** ______________________________

____

68. **Flashover (245)** ______________________________

____

69. **Rollover (248)** ______________________________

____

70. **Backdraft (249)** ______________________________

____

71. **Smoke Explosion (250)** ______________________________

____

72. **Tactical Ventilation (253)** ______________________________

____

True/False

Write True or False on the blanks provided; if False, write the correct statement on the lines provided.

________ 1. The most commonly found oxidizer is the oxygen found in the air. (208)

____

____

________ 2. All energy remains in the same form until it is expended. (209)

____

____

_______ 3. The energy necessary for ignition of a fire is only provided by an external source. (210-212)

_______ 4. Autoignition temperature is sometimes higher than a fuel's piloted ignition temperature. (212)

_______ 5. Combustion is a chemical reaction that can occur without fire. (212)

_______ 6. Most products of combustion are toxic and present a significant threat to human life. (215)

_______ 7. Smoke may contain unburned fuel. (216)

_______ 8. Thermal energy is never in transit from one location to another. (216)

_______ 9. Conduction is the reason firefighters may feel an increase in temperature when working in a flow path. (222)

_______ 10. Heat release rate (HHR) decreases when ventilation is limited. (224)

_______ 11. The primary consideration for ignition of solid fuels is surface-to-mass ratio. (228)

_______ 12. Nonflaming combustion can continue at extremely low concentrations when the surrounding temperature is low. (231)

____

____

_______ 13. Isolated flames may be observed moving through the gas layer during the incipient stage of a fire. (245)

____

____

_______ 14. Temperatures in a decaying compartment fire do not remain high even after heat release rate drops. (246)

____

____

Fill in the Blank

Write the correct answer on the blanks provided.

1. While at a fire scene you notice that fuel sources close to areas already on fire are igniting faster than those farther away from the fire. What you are noticing is a result of the _______________released during combustion. (214)

2. Fire fighting requires the correct use of SCBA to protect firefighters from gases, vapors, and solid particulates that are created during fire ground operations. This product of combustion that includes toxic and flammable gases, vapors, and particulates is most commonly referred to as _______________. (215-216)

3. Firefighters wear personal protective equipment during emergency operations to protect from a visible product of combustion. This product is called ____________________ and becomes hotter and less luminous when mixed with proper amounts of oxygen. (216)

4. There are many fire fighting methods, but the most common is cooling fuel with water. This method is called _______________ and works to reduce the temperature of fuel to the point that it does not produce sufficient vapor to burn. (250)

5. Of the fire fighting methods available to use one method is the simplest. However, allowing a fire to burn until all the fuel is consumed, often called ______________is not always desirable. (251)

6. Some fire fighting methods will only work on specific types of fuels. For example, the method of __________________ does not work if a fuel is self-oxidizing. (251)

Identification

Write the correct answers on the blanks provided.

Stages of Fire Development (241-247)

Identify the fire stage in the image below.

1. ______________________________

2. ______________________________

3. ____

4. ____

5

Matching

Write the correct answers on the blanks provided.

Science of Fire

Match the definition with the fire term listed. Each choice will be used once.

_______ 1. A reaction that emits energy as it occurs (210)

_______ 2. Type of ignition that occurs without any external flame or spark (210-212)

_______ 3. When a substance changes from one type of matter into another (208)

_______ 4. Mode of combustion that occurs more slowly at a lower temperature producing a smoldering glow in a material's surface (212)

_______ 5. Form of heat transfer through and between solids (220)

_______ 6. The term that represents the amount of energy an object can release at some point in the future (209)

_______ 7. The most common form of ignition that occurs when a mixture of fuel and oxygen encounter an external heat source with sufficient heat to start the combustion process (210)

_______ 8. Mode of combustion that produces visible flame above a material's surface (212)

_______ 9. Form of heat transfer by circulation or movement of fluid (221)

_______ 10. Heat transfer by the transmission of energy as an electromagnetic wave without an intervening medium (222)

_______ 11. When a substance remains chemically the same but changes in size, shape, or appearance (208)

_______ 12. The term that represents the energy possessed by a moving object (209)

_______ 13. A reaction that absorbs energy as it occurs (210)

A. Kinetic
B. Piloted
C. Flaming
D. Potential
E. Radiation
F. Convection
G. Conduction
H. Exothermic
I. Nonflaming
J. Autoignition
K. Endothermic
L. Physical change
M. Chemical reaction

Multiple Choice

Write the correct answers on the blanks provided.

_____ 1. All forms of fire involve a heat-producing chemical reaction between: (208)

A. fuel and an oxidizer.
B. an oxidizer and light.
C. fuel and ambient heat.
D. ambient heat and light.

_____ 2. What product of combustion prevents the body from using oxygen on the cellular level? (216)

A. Smoke
B. Thermal energy
C. Hydrogen cyanide
D. Carbon monoxide

_____ 3. What product of combustion increases respiratory rate? (216)

A. Flame
B. Smoke
C. Carbon dioxide
D. Hydrogen cyanide

_____ 4. Which of the following BEST describes why firefighters must wear SCBA during overhaul? (216)

A. Smoke is not like other flammable gases; it will not burn or explode.
B. Hazardous concentrations within short-term exposure limits are present.
C. Volume and density of smoke is reduced, and the hazard is eliminated.
D. Hazardous concentrations of smoke may be present outside the structure.

_____ 5. What method of electrical energy is defined as particles that can be formed and spatter away from the point of arcing? (219)

A. Sparking
B. Overcurrent
C. Resistance heating
D. Spontaneous ignition

_____ 6. The movement of two surfaces against each other creates what source of thermal energy? (219)

A. Potential
B. Chemical
C. Electrical
D. Mechanical

_____ 7. Which of the following disrupts the point-to-point transfer of heat? (221)

A. Fuel

B. Oxygen

C. Passive agents

D. Insulating materials

_____ 8. Which of the following BEST describes the influence of exposed surfaces on radiant heat? (223)

A. Creating a vacuum will stop radiant heat.

B. Light materials emit and absorb heat more effectively than dark materials.

C. Increasing distance between the heat source and exposed surfaces increases the effect of radiant heat.

D. Temperature differences between the heat source and exposed surface has a major effect on heat transfer.

_____ 9. Which of the following influences how easily a liquid can be ignited? (226)

A. Volatility

B. Miscibility

C. Flash point

D. Vapor pressure

_____ 10. Which of the following BEST describes the impact of an extinguishing agent when trying to extinguish flaming combustion? (234)

A. It forms an unstable product.

B. It creates a faster chemical reaction.

C. It terminates the combustion reaction.

D. It burns more oxygen in a short amount of time.

_____ 11. What thermal property of a compartment maintains the temperature by absorbing and releasing large amounts of heat slowly? (240)

A. Insulation

B. Retention

C. Passive agents

D. Heat reflectivity

_____ 12. What common element of flashover requires the combustion to be in an enclosed space? (247)

A. Rapidity

B. Compartment

C. Transition in fire development

D. Ignition of all exposed surfaces

_____ 13. Which of the following is an air flow indicator of a possible flashover? (248)

A. Darkened windows
B. Rapidly increasing temperature
C. Isolated flames in hot gas layer
D. High velocity and turbulent air flow

_____ 14. Which of the following is an air flow indicator of a possible backdraft? (249)

A. Optically dense smoke
B. Turbulent smoke discharge
C. Fire confined to a void space
D. Neutral plane rising and lowering

Short Answer

Write the correct answers on the blanks provided.

1. List the three types of thermal energy and give a brief description of how these methods could occur. (217-219)

____
____
____
____
____
____
____
____

2. Briefly explain what impacts heat transfer rate. (219)

____
____
____
____
____

3. What are the seven factors that affect fire development? (234-235)

4. Briefly explain the difference between a fuel-controlled fire and a ventilation-controlled fire. (239)

Crossword Puzzle

Across

5. A fire with limited ventilation in which the heat release rate or growth is limited by the amount of oxygen available to the fire (NFPA® 921)
7. First stage of the burning process in a compartment in which the substance being oxidized is producing some heat, but the heat has not spread to other substances nearby
10. A fire with adequate oxygen in which the heat release rate and growth rate are determined by the characteristics of the fuel, such as quantity and geometry (NFPA® 921)
13. Outcome of combustion in a confined space in which gases tend to form into layers, according to temperature, with the hottest gases found at the ceiling and the coolest gases at floor level
15. Transfer of heat through or between solids that are in direct contact
16. A chemical process of oxidation that occurs at a rate fast enough to produce heat and usually light in the form of either a glow or flame (NFPA® 921)
18. Initiation of combustion by heat but without a spark or flame (NFPA® 921)
19. Materials that absorb heat but do not participate actively in the combustion process

Down

1. A condition where the unburned fire gases that have accumulated at the top of a compartment ignite and flames propagate through the hot-gas layer or across the ceiling
2. Model used to explain the elements/conditions necessary for combustion; represented by heat, oxygen, and fuel
3. Chemical decomposition of a solid material by heating
4. Form of fire gas ignition; the ignition of accumulated flammable products of combustion and air that are within their flammable range
6. Any material that readily yields oxygen or other oxidizing gas, or that readily reacts to promote or initiate combustion of combustible materials (NFPA® 400)
8. A relatively thin layer of flowing hot gases that develops under a horizontal surface (e.g., ceiling) as a result of plume impingement and the flowing gas being forced to move horizontally (NFPA® 921)
9. Moment when a mixture of fuel and oxygen encounters an external heat (ignition) source with sufficient heat or thermal energy to start the combustion reaction
10. Model of the four elements/conditions required to have a fire; represented by fuel, heat, oxygen, and self-sustaining chemical chain reaction
11. A rapid transition from the growth stage to the fully developed stage
12. The explosive burning of heated gases that occurs when oxygen is introduced into a compartment that has a high concentration of flammable gases and a depleted supply of oxygen due to an existing fire
14. Heat transfer by way of electromagnetic energy (NFPA® 921)

Down

17. Heat transfer by circulation within a medium such as a gas or a liquid (NFPA® 921)

Chapter 6

Firefighter Personal Protective Equipment

Firefighter I

Terms

Write the definition of the terms below on the blanks provided.

1. **Personal Protective Equipment (PPE) (259)** ______________________________

2. **Structural Fire Fighting (261)** ______________________________

3. **Proximity Fire Fighting (261)** ______________________________

4. **Helmet (264)** ______________________________

5. **Protective Hood (266)** ______________________________

6. **Protective Coat (266)** ______________________________

7. **Protective Trousers (267)** ______________________________

8. **Protective Gloves (267)** ______________________________

9. **Fire Fighting Boots (267)** ______________________________

10. **Hearing Protection (270)** ____________________

11. **Personal Alert Safety System (PASS) (270)** ____________________

12. **Respiratory Hazards (281)** ____________________

13. **Oxygen-Deficient Atmosphere (282)** ____________________

14. **Hypoxia (282)** ____________________

15. **Pulmonary Edema (283)** ____________________

16. **Asphyxiation (283)** ____________________

17. **Particulate (283)** ____________________

18. **Air-Purifying Respirator (APR) (284)** ____________________

19. **Powered Air-Purifying Respirator (PAPR) (284)** ____________________

20. **Gas (284)** ____________________

21. **Vapor (284)** ____

____

22. **Airborne Pathogens (287)** ____

____

23. **High-Efficiency Particulate Air (HEPA) Filter (287)** ____

____

24. **Open-Circuit Self-Contained Breathing Apparatus (289)** ____

____

25. **Closed-Circuit Self-Contained Breathing Apparatus (289)** ____

____

26. **Qualitative Fit Test (QLFT) (292)** ____

____

27. **Quantitative Fit Test (QNFT) (292)** ____

____

28. ***Code of Federal Regulations (CFR)* (293)** ____

____

29. **Hydrostatic Test (303)** ____

____

30. **Cascade System (307)** ____

____

31. **Permissible Exposure Limits (PEL) (314)** ____

____

32. **Search Line (315)** ____

____

True/False

Write True or False on the blanks provided; if False, write the correct statement on the lines provided.

_______ 1. PPE is designed to protect from hazards and minimize risk of injury and fatality. (259-261)

_______ 2. Inspecting, cleaning, and maintaining the condition of PPE is the responsibility of the shift supervisor. (277)

_______ 3. All cleaning of PPE is performed at the local station. (278)

_______ 4. Supplied air respirators (SARs) are used when a firefighter must be in a hazardous area for a long period of time and there is no danger that fire may damage the hose. (289)

_______ 5. Closed-circuit SCBAs use compressed air. (289)

_______ 6. In an open-circuit SCBA exhaled air stays in the system and is reused. (289)

_______ 7. Air-purifying respirators (APRs) remove contaminants by passing ambient air through the filter, canister, and cartridge. (293)

_______ 8. Taste and smell can be clues that an APR is losing its effectiveness. (295)

_______ 9. Storing requirements for respiratory equipment may depend on size, available compartments on apparatus, and manufacturer's instructions. (296)

_______ 10. SCBA stored in cases can only be donned using the over-the-coat method. (298)

_______ 11. The facepiece lens of protective breathing apparatus should be inspected for scratches, abrasions, holes, cracks, or heat damage during daily/weekly inspections. (303)

_______ 12. The facepiece of protective breathing apparatus can be dried with paper towels. (305)

_______ 13. The type of material used to construct an SCBA air cylinder determines the frequency of hydrostatic testing of the cylinder. (306)

_______ 14. Replacing SCBA cylinders is always a two-person job. (311)

_______ 15. In an IDLH atmosphere, firefighters are required to work in teams of two or more. (313)

_______ 16. Controlled breathing allows for efficient air use in an IDLH atmosphere. (315)

_______ 17. Egress paths are located once a firefighter is inside an IDLH atmosphere. (315)

Matching

Write the correct answers on the blanks provided.

Personal Protective Equipment

Match the type of personal protective equipment listed with the brief definition below. Each choice will only be used once.

_______ 1. Clothing designed to meet the needs of specific rescue operations, including: technical rescue, ice rescue, and hazardous materials incidents. (274-276)

_______ 2. Clothing designed according to the requirements of NFPA® 1977 and includes: gloves, goggles, jackets, jumpsuits, face/neck shrouds; as well as a fire shelter and other equipment. (270)

_______ 3. Clothing designed to increase visibility to motorists, includes traffic vests. (273)

_______ 4. Clothing worn to protect against exposure to infectious bodily fluids that must meet the requirements of NFPA® 1999. (274)

_______ 5. Clothing that according to the requirements of NFPA® 1971 must include: retroreflective trim, wristlets, collars, a closure system, and a drag rescue device. (276)

_______ 6. Clothing designed to meet the requirements of NFPA® 1975 and intended to identify wearer as a member of the organization and provide a layer of protection against direct flame contact. (276)

A. Structural fire fighting protective clothing

B. Wildland personal protective clothing

C. Roadway operations clothing

D. Emergency medical protective clothing

E. Special protective clothing

F. Station/work uniform

Respiratory Hazards

Match the respiratory hazard with the brief definition below. Each choice will only be used once.

_______ 1. Hazard which can cause superheated air to damage the respiratory tract, a serious decrease in blood pressure, and a failure of the circulatory system. (283)

_______ 2. Hazard which may be inhaled, ingested, or absorbed into the body; includes formaldehyde, phosgene, and nitrous gases. (284-285)

_______ 3. Hazard caused by disease-causing microorganisms suspended in the air. (287)

_______ 4. Hazard produced during incidents involving industrial occupancies, spills from transportation accidents, and leaks from storage containers. (285-286)

A. Oxygen deficiency

B. Elevated temperatures

C. Particulate contaminants

D. Gases and vapors

E. Nonfire gases and vapors

F. Airborne pathogens

_________ 5. Hazard most commonly caused by combustion which consumes and displaces oxygen present in the atmosphere. (282)

_________ 6. Hazard produced by vehicle exhaust emissions, chemical reactions, heated metals or metal compounds, and combustion. (283)

Multiple Choice

Write the correct answers on the blanks provided.

_____ 1. Which of the following BEST describes the purpose of an open-circuit SCBA facepiece assembly? (292)

A. It permits limited communication.
B. It holds the facepiece snugly against the face.
C. It provides fresh breathing air while protecting the eyes and face.
D. It deflects exhalations away from the lens, reducing fogging or condensation.

_____ 2. Which of the following is prohibited by NFPA® 1500 because it prevents a complete facepiece seal? (292)

A. Intercom devices
B. Ear protection devices
C. Beards or facial hair
D. Protective hoods that fold

_____ 3. As defined by the *Code of Federal Regulations,* the R in particle filter degradation means: (294)

A. resistant to oil.
B. not resistant to oil.
C. resistant to nitrogen based gases.
D. not resistant to nitrogen based gases.

_____ 4. Which of the following BEST describes how to offset wearer limitations of respiratory protection? (296)

A. Proper exercise and training
B. Proper maintenance and training
C. Through constant training and proper fit-testing of facepieces
D. Through frequent and proper inspections, care, and maintenance

_____ 5. What respiratory protection equipment limitation can proportionately reduce working time? (296)

A. Limited visibility
B. Decreased mobility
C. Decreased endurance
D. Low air cylinder pressure

_____ 6. Which of the following BEST describes differences that may be found in SCBA facepieces? (301)

A. The location of regulator may differ.

B. The chin cup and harness may be located differently.

C. The exhalation valve may be located in a different place.

D. Straps may need to be extended differently depending on model.

_____ 7. Which piece of protective breathing apparatus must be inspected for abrasions, cuts, tears, or heat or chemical-induced damage? (303)

A. Hose threads

B. Facepiece nosecup

C. Breathing air cylinder valve

D. Backplate and harness assembly

_____ 8. Which piece of protective respiratory equipment hardware must be inspected for cleanliness, proper attachment, and damage? (305)

A. Regulator

B. Low-pressure alarm

C. Stand-alone PASS device

D. Pressure indicator gauges

_____ 9. Which type of SCBA system provides an endless source of breathing air to any floor within a structure from a ground level connection? (310)

A. SCBA cylinder

B. Mobile fill station

C. Stationary fill station

D. Firefighting breathing air replenishment system (FBARS)

Short Answer

Write the correct answers on the blanks provided.

1. List three specific safety considerations a firefighter must be aware of when using PPE. (280)

2. Explain the three criteria that must be met to allow a rapid intervention crew or team (RIC/RIT) rescuing a trapped or incapacitated firefighter to refill an unshielded SCBA cylinder. (307)

3. Compare and contrast the difference between nonemergency exit indicators and emergency exit indicators. (313)

Crossword Puzzle

Across

3. Disease-causing microorganisms (viruses, bacteria, or fungi) that are suspended in the air
5. Activities required for rescue, fire suppression, and property conservation in structures, vehicles, vessels, and similar types of properties
9. Compressible substance, with no specific volume, that tends to assume the shape of the container
10. Accumulation of fluids in the lungs
12. Respirator that removes contaminants by passing ambient air through a filter, cartridge, or canister
13. Nonload-bearing rope that is anchored to a safe, exterior location and attached to a firefighter during search operations to act as a safety line
15. Fatal condition caused by severe oxygen deficiency and an excess of carbon monoxide and/or other gases in the blood
16. Respirator fit test that measures the wearer's response to a test agent, such as irritant smoke or odorous vapor
17. Gaseous form of a substance that is normally in a solid or liquid state at room temperature and pressure
19. Legal term for the maximum amount of a chemical substance or other hazard that an employee can be exposed to
20. Very small particle of solid material, such as dust, that is suspended in the atmosphere
21. Potentially fatal condition caused by lack of oxygen
22. Worn by firefighters to provide protection from falling objects, side blows, elevated temperatures, and heated water
23. Respiratory filter that is certified to remove at least 99.97 % of monodisperse particles of 0.3 micrometers in diameter

Down

1. Device that limits noise-induced hearing loss when firefighters are exposed to extremely loud environments
2. Three or more large, interconnected air cylinders, from which smaller SCBA cylinders are recharged
4. Exposure to conditions that create a hazard to the respiratory system
6. Fit test in which instruments measure the amount of a test agent that has leaked into the respirator from the ambient atmosphere
7. Worn to protect the lower torso and legs during emergency operations
8. Electronic lack-of-motion sensor that sounds a loud alarm when a firefighter becomes motionless
11. Activities required for rescue, fire suppression, and property conservation at fires that produce high radiant, conductive, or convective heat
14. Designed to protect the firefighter's ears, neck, and face from heat and debris
18. Worn during fire fighting, rescue, and extrication operations

Across

24. Testing method that uses water under pressure to check the integrity of pressure vessels

25. Atmosphere containing less than the normal 19.5 percent oxygen

Chapter 7

Portable Fire Extinguishers

Firefighter I

Terms

Write the definition of the terms below on the blanks provided.

1. **Fire Extinguisher (340)** ______________________________

____

2. **Dry Chemical (341)** ______________________________

____

3. **Dry Powder (341)** ______________________________

____

4. **Wet Chemical System (342)** ______________________________

____

5. **Extinguishing Agent (342)** ______________________________

____

6. **Saponification (342)** ______________________________

____

7. **Water-Mist (345)** ______________________________

____

8. **Deionized Water (346)** ______________________________

____

9. **Air-Aspirating Foam Nozzle (346)** ______________________________

____

10. **Halogenated Extinguishing Agents (347)** ______________________________

____

11. **Corrosive (349)** ______________________________

____

True/False

Write True or False on the blanks provided; if False, write the correct statement on the lines provided.

_______ 1. The five classes of portable fire extinguishers match the five classes of fire. (340)

____

____

_______ 2. Class B fires can be extinguished with water, water-based agents, and dry chemicals. (341)

____

____

_______ 3. Dry chemical and dry powder extinguishers are essentially the same. (341)

____

____

_______ 4. Extinguishing agents use only one method to extinguish a fire. (342)

____

____

_______ 5. Wet chemical stored-pressure extinguishers are intended for use on Class K fires. (346)

____

____

_______ 6. Carbon dioxide (CO_2) extinguishers can be found in both handheld and wheeled units. (348)

____

____

_______ 7. When using a wheeled dry chemical unit, allow a few minutes for the unit to fully pressurize after introducing the gas before opening the nozzle. (350)

____

____

_______ 8. When using a portable fire extinguisher always approach the fire with the wind at your back. (355)

____

____

_______ 9. If a fire is not reduced in size after using an entire extinguisher, try using another entire extinguisher before reassessing the situation. (356)

____

____

_______ 10. Stand empty portable fire extinguishers up to signal to others that the unit is empty. (356)

____

____

_______ 11. Privately owned extinguishers have no inspection regulations. (357)

____

____

_______ 12. Some cleaning solvents may damage plastic parts of portable fire extinguishers. (358)

____

____

_______ 13. Dry chemical extinguishers must be emptied and refilled every six years. (358)

____

____

Identification

Write the correct answers on the blanks provided.

Extinguisher Ratings (353)

Identify the extinguisher rating pictograph in the image below.

1. ______________________

2. ______________________

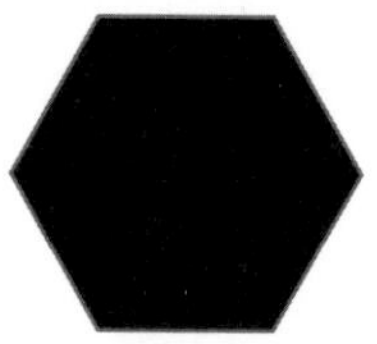

3. ______________________

4. ______________________

5. ______________________

Matching

Write the correct answers on the blanks provided.

Classifications of Portable Fire Extinguishers

Match the type of fire to be extinguished with the portable fire extinguisher classification. Each choice will be used once.

_______ 1. Fires that involve flammable, combustible liquids and gases (341)

_______ 2. Fires that involve energized electrical equipment (341)

_______ 3. Fires that involve combustible cooking oils (342)

_______ 4. Fires that involve combustible metals and alloys (341)

_______ 5. Fires that involve ordinary combustibles (341)

A. Class A
B. Class B
C. Class C
D. Class D
E. Class K

Methods of Extinguishing

Match the definition with the extinguishing method. Each choice will be used once.

_______ 1. Interrupts chemical chain reaction in the burning process (342)

_______ 2. Excludes oxygen from the burning process (342)

_______ 3. Reduces burning material below ignition temperature (342)

_______ 4. Forms oxygen-excluding soapy foam surface (342)

A. Cooling
B. Chain breaking
C. Saponification
D. Smothering

Multiple Choice

Write the correct answers on the blanks provided.

_____ 1. What classification of portable fire extinguisher is used on fires that involve ordinary combustibles? (341)

A. Class A
B. Class B
C. Class D
D. Class K

_____ 2. Once the power supply is turned off in a Class C fire it can be: (341)

A. allowed to burn itself out.
B. treated like a Class A or Class B fire.
C. extinguished with a dry powder extinguisher.
D. extinguished with a wet chemical stored-pressure extinguisher.

_____ 3. Which method of extinguishing works by interrupting the chemical chain reaction in the burning process? (342)

A. Cooling
B. Smothering
C. Saponification
D. Chain breaking

_____ 4. What expelling mechanism works using compressed inert gas that is contained in a separate cartridge on the side of the container? (343)

A. Scoop
B. Manual pump
C. Stored pressure
D. Pressure cartridge

_____ 5. What type of portable fire extinguisher uses deionized water as an agent and can be used on Class C fires? (346)

A. Pump-type water
B. Carbon dioxide (CO_2)
C. Water-mist stored-pressure
D. Wet chemical stored-pressure

_____ 6. What type of portable fire extinguisher was developed to replace halogenated extinguishing agents? (347)

A. Clean agent
B. Pump-type water
C. Carbon dioxide (CO_2)
D. Wet chemical stored-pressure

_____ 7. What type of portable fire extinguisher discharge is usually accompanied by dry ice crystals? (348)

A. Clean agent
B. Pump-type water
C. Carbon dioxide (CO_2)
D. Wet chemical stored-pressure

_____ 8. What type of portable fire extinguisher was developed to control and extinguish fires involving Class D combustible metals? (350)

A. Dry powder
B. Dry chemical
C. Pump-type water
D. Wet chemical stored-pressure

Short Answer

Write the correct answers on the lines provided.

1. List at least four of the factors that must be considered when determining if a portable fire extinguisher will be effective in extinguishing a fire. (354)

____

____

____

____

2. What does each step in the PASS acronym stand for? (355)

____

____

____

____

Crossword Puzzle

Across

6. A fire extinguisher capable of atomizing water through a special applicator
7. Extinguishing agent suitable for use on combustible metal fires
8. Portable fire fighting device designed to combat incipient fires
10. The most effective appliance for the generation of low-expansion foam

Down

1. Water from which ionic salts, minerals, and impurities have been removed by ion-exchange
2. Extinguishing system usually installed in range hoods and associated ducting where grease may accumulate
3. A phenomenon that occurs when mixtures of alkaline-based chemicals and certain cooking oils come into contact resulting in the formation of a soapy film
4. Capable of causing corrosion by gradually eroding, rusting, or destroying a material
5. Extinguishing system often used to protect areas containing volatile flammable liquids
9. Any substance used for the purpose of controlling or extinguishing a fire

1
2
3
4
5
6
7
8
9
10

Chapter 8

Ropes, Webbing, and Knots

Firefighter I

Terms

Write the definition of the terms below on the blanks provided.

1. **Life-safety Rope (370)**____________________

2. **Utility Rope (370)** ____________________

3. **Block Creel Construction (371)** ____________________

4. **Impact Load (371)** ____________________

5. **Synthetic Fiber Rope (373)**____________________

6. **Natural Fiber Rope (373)** ____________________

7. **Kernmantle Rope (374)** ____________________

8. **Dynamic Rope (374)** ____________________

9. **Static Rope (374)**____________________

10. **Laid Rope (374)**

11. **Braided Rope (375)**

12. **Braid-on-braid Rope (375)**

13. **Rope Log (381)**

14. **Webbing (381)**

15. **Ladder Belt (382)**

16. **Knot (384)**

17. **Working End (384)**

18. **Running Part (384)**

19. **Standing Part (384)**

20. **Overhand Safety Knot (384)**

21. **Hitch (384)** ___

22. **Bowline Knot (387)** ___

23. **Half-Hitch (387)** ___

24. **Clove Hitch (388)** ___

25. **Handcuff (Rescue) Knot (388)** ___

26. **Becket Bend (389)** ___

27. **Tag Line (390)** ___

28. **Mechanical Advantage (390)** ___

True/False

Write True or False on the blanks provided; if False, write the correct statement on the lines provided.

___ 1. NFPA® 1973 lists life-safety rope regulations. (371)

___ 2. There is no NFPA® standard that lists requirements for utility rope. (372)

_______ 3. NFPA® 1983 requires that all types of rope have a rope log. (372)

_______ 4. Natural fiber rope is resistant to water, mildew, mold, and rotting. (373)

_______ 5. Synthetic fiber rope is very strong yet lightweight. (373)

_______ 6. Some fuzziness in a kernmantle construction rope is normal. (376)

_______ 7. Natural fiber and synthetic fiber ropes are washed in the same way. (379-381)

_______ 8. A rope log is usually stored in a pocket sewn into the side of a rope storage bag. (381)

_______ 9. Webbing used for life safety must be NFPA® compliant. (381)

_______ 10. Both life safety and utility webbing are regulated by NFPA® standards. (382-384)

_______ 11. The load carrying ability of a rope must exceed the weight of the object hoisted or stabilized. (390)

Matching

Write the correct answers on the blanks provided.

Types of Rope

Match the definition with the correct type of rope listed. Each choice will be used once.

_______ 1. This rope is constructed of a braided sheath over a core of main load-bearing strands. (374)

_______ 2. This rope is constructed by uniformly intertwining strands together in a diagonally overlapping pattern. (375)

_______ 3. This rope is constructed by twisting fibers together to form strands, then twisting the strands together to make the final rope. (374)

_______ 4. This rope is constructed of a braided core enclosed in a braided, herringbone-patterned sheath. (375)

A. Laid rope

B. Braided rope

C. Kernmantle rope

D. Braid-on-braid rope

Types of Webbing

Match the definition with the correct type of webbing listed. Each choice will be used once.

_______ 1. This webbing fastens around the waist, under the thighs or buttocks and over the shoulders; it is rated for loads up to 600 pounds (2.67 kN). (382)

_______ 2. This webbing fastens around the waist and under the thighs or buttocks and is rated for a load up to 600 pounds (2.67 kN). (382)

_______ 3. This webbing is used for a variety of uses and is not regulated by any specific standard. (384)

_______ 4. This webbing is known as a seat harness and is intended for emergency escape with a load of up to 300 pounds (1.33 kN). (382)

A. Utility webbing

B. Class I life-safety webbing

C. Class II life-safety webbing

D. Class III life-safety webbing

Knot Parts and Elements

Match the definition with the correct knot part or element listed. Each choice will be used once.

_______ 1. This aspect of the knot is the section between the working end and the running part. (384)

_______ 2. This aspect of the knot is formed by bending the rope back on itself while keeping the sides parallel. (385)

_______ 3. This aspect of the knot is used to tie the knot or hitch. (384)

_______ 4. This aspect of the knot is made by further bending one side of a loop. (385)

_______ 5. This aspect of the knot is the free end used for hoisting or pulling. (384)

_______ 6. This aspect of the knot is made by crossing the side of the bight over the standing part. (385)

A. Bight
B. Loop
C. Round turn
D. Standing part
E. Running part
F. Working end

Firefighter I

Multiple Choice

Write the correct answers on the blanks provided.

_____ 1. A life safety rope should be removed from service or replaced if: (371)
A. it has no abrasions or visible damage.
B. it has been subjected to any impact load.
C. it has not been exposed to heat or direct flame.
D. it has passed inspection conducted by qualified personnel.

_____ 2. According to NFPA® 1983 a rope log must include: (372)
A. purchase date.
B. possible uses for rope.
C. local cleaning protocols.
D. types of objects that can be hoisted with rope.

_____ 3. Which of the following is a disadvantage of natural fiber rope? (373)
A. Melts when exposed to heat
B. Very strong yet lightweight
C. Resistance to mildew and rotting
D. Deteriorates when exposed to chemicals

_____ 4. All of the following ropes except _____ are inspected by looking for soft, mushy spots. (376-378)

A. braided rope
B. kernmantle rope
C. natural fiber laid rope
D. synthetic fiber laid rope

_____ 5. Which of the following can make a rope easy to transport and protect it from abrasion? (381)

A. Rope bag
B. Rope carabiner
C. Rope drying rack
D. Rope washing machine

_____ 6. Which of the following pieces of equipment connects ropes to other mechanical gear? (390)

A. Pulley
B. Tag line
C. Carabiner
D. Webbing

_____ 7. Which of the following is NOT a hoisting safety guideline? (391)

A. Use hand-over-hand method
B. Use pulley system for heavy objects
C. Work in teams when working from heights
D. Always hoist tools and equipment, even if hand carrying would work

_____ 8. Which of the following is NOT a hoisting safety guideline? (391)

A. Ensure personnel are clear from hoisting area
B. Choose closest location to object before hoisting
C. Use edge roller to protect rope from physical damage
D. Secure nozzles of charged hoselines to prevent accidental discharge

_____ 9. Which of the following is traditionally used to establish a control zone perimeter? (394)

A. Utility rope
B. Life safety rope
C. Utility webbing
D. Life safety webbing

_____ 10. During stabilization, where is the rope or webbing first secured? (396)

A. A parked apparatus
B. A strong, stationary object
C. The object being stabilized
D. The object next to the one being stabilized

Short Answer

Write the correct answers on the blanks provided.

1. What are the four basic aspects of rope maintenance? (376)

____

____

____

____

2. What specific actions can firefighters take to care for rope? (378-379)

____

____

____

____

____

____

____

____

Crossword Puzzle

Across

4. Rope designed exclusively for rescue and other emergency operations
6. Rope designed to stretch under load, reducing the shock of impact after a fall
7. Belt with a hook that secures the firefighter to the ladder
9. Free end of the rope used for hoisting, pulling, or belaying
11. Device used for creating anchors and lashings, or for packaging patients and rescuers
13. Rope designed for any use except rescue
14. Rope that consists of a protective shield over the load-bearing core strands
16. Utility rope made of manila, sisal, or cotton
17. Knot well suited for joining ropes of unequal diameters or joining a rope and a chain
18. Rope constructed by twisting several groups of individual strands together
20. Rope made from continuous, synthetic fibers running the entire length of the rope
21. Non-load-bearing rope attached to a hoisted object to help steer it in a desired direction, prevent it from spinning or snagging on obstructions, or act as a safety line
22. Knot principally used to attach a rope to an object such as a pole, post, or hose
23. Dynamic and sudden load placed on a rope
24. Knot tied in a bight with two adjustable loops in opposing directions

Down

1. Middle of the rope, between the working end and the running part
2. Advantage created when levers, pulleys, and tools are used to make work easier during rope rescue or while lifting heavy objects
3. Rope that consists of a braided core enclosed in a braided, herringbone patterned sheath
5. Knot typically used to stabilize long objects that are being hoisted
8. Rope constructed by uniformly intertwining strands of rope together
10. Method of manufacturing rope without any knots or splices
11. End of the rope used to tie a knot
12. Supplemental knot tied to prevent the primary knot from failing
15. Knot used to form a loop
19. Record of all use, maintenance, and inspection throughout a rope's working life
20. Rope designed not to stretch under load

1
2
3
4
5
6
7
8
9
10
11
12
13
14
15
16
17
18
19
20
21
22
23
24

Chapter 9

Structural Search, Victim Removal, and Firefighter Survival

Terms

Write the definition of the terms below on the blanks provided.

1. **Preincident Survey (422)** ____________________

2. **Target Hazard (423)** ____________________

3. **Size-Up (425)** ____________________

4. **Sounding (426)** ____________________

5. **Freelance (426)** ____________________

6. **Primary Search (430)** ____________________

7. **Secondary Search (430)** ____________________

8. **Rekindle (431)** ____________________

9. **MAYDAY (444)** ______________________________

10. **Low-Pressure Alarm (446)** ______________________________

11. **Rapid Intervention Crew or Team (RIC/RIT) (447)** ______________________________

12. **Point of No Return (448)** ______________________________

True/False

Write True or False on the blanks provided; if False, write the correct statement on the lines provided.

_______ 1. Size-up is used to observe an incident scene to answer questions such as: what has happened and what is happening. (425)

_______ 2. Situational awareness can help firefighters determine if a building is occupied. (425)

_______ 3. One way to determine if fire is on the other side of a door is for firefighters to slightly crack open the door. (426)

_______ 4. Do not enter a structure in which survivors are not likely to be found. (426)

_________ 5. During a structural search firefighters should work individually to find victims and save lives. (427)

____

____

_________ 6. Firefighters should maintain contact with the wall, a hoseline, or a search line when visibility is obscured. (428)

____

____

_________ 7. Firefighters should enter the immediately dangerous to life and health atmosphere as soon as arriving on scene, sometimes without checking in with a supervisor. (428)

____

____

_________ 8. Assume a structure is occupied if there are no witnesses. (428)

____

____

_________ 9. During the primary search, firefighters check for victims and assess fire conditions. (430)

____

____

_________ 10. A secondary search is performed by the same personnel who participate in the primary search. (431)

____

____

_________ 11. On the fire floor, firefighters should start the search as close to the fire as possible. (432)

____

____

_________ 12. Search teams can control egress passageways by closing adjacent doors after a search. (432)

____

____

________ 13. Opening doors and windows can disrupt ventilation efforts. (434)

________ 14. The cradle-in-arms lift/carry is used to rescue unconscious adults. (441)

________ 15. Firefighters should know personal physical limitations in order to be able to withdraw before being incapacitated. (445)

________ 16. MAYDAY is a term used whenever a firefighter is in immediate danger. (447)

________ 17. An evacuation signal is only given as a radio message. (448)

________ 18. Filtering toxic air through a protective hood in a MAYDAY situation will remove toxins. (450)

________ 19. When escaping as a team, firefighters should leave the hose nozzle behind when withdrawing. (451)

________ 20. The SCBA-first (through a wall) method of escape should only be used as a last resort. (452)

Matching

Write the correct answers on the blanks provided.

Search Methods

Match the definition with the type of search method listed. Each choice will be used once.

_________ 1. This search method is used to conduct a primary search in a large or complex area filled with smoke. (434)

_________ 2. This search method uses a system where the team leaders stay anchored at the door while other team members spread out in a room. (434)

_________ 3. This search method is used to locate both victims and hidden fires. (437)

_________ 4. This search method consists of guidelines such as: follow a systematic pattern during a search and start the search as close to the fire as possible on the fire floor. (431)

A. General search method

B. Oriented-search method

C. Wide-area-search method

D. Thermal-imager-search method

Victim Removal Methods

Match the definition with the correct victim removal method listed. Each choice will be used once.

_________ 1. This removal method enables two rescuers to carry conscious or unconscious victims. (442)

_________ 2. This removal method operates on the principle that most victims can evacuate a structure alone. (439)

_________ 3. This removal method is used to carry children or small, conscious adults. (442)

_________ 4. This removal method is useful when heat and smoke force a firefighter to stay low. (441)

_________ 5. This removal method is commonly used in hospitals, high-rises, and high hazard industrial sites. (440)

A. Shelter-in-place

B. Self-evacuation

C. Webbing drag

D. Seat lift/carry

E. Cradle-in-arms lift/carry

Firefighter I

MAYDAY Events

Match the definition with the correct type of MAYDAY event listed. Each choice will be used once.

_______ 1. This MAYDAY event is caused when a firefighter loses contact with a partner, the hoseline or search line, or the orientation point. (446)

_______ 2. This MAYDAY event occurs when a firefighter is caught on exposed wires or debris. (446)

_______ 3. This MAYDAY event is created when a rapid rise in temperature exceeds their PPE's level of protection. (446)

_______ 4. This MAYDAY event can occur when a structure has been intentionally damaged to create traps for responders. (446)

_______ 5. This MAYDAY event can be caused by a firefighter running out of air. (446)

A. Entanglement
B. Collapse/trapped
C. Lost/disoriented
D. Air emergencies
E. Thermal emergencies

Multiple Choice

Write the correct answers on the blanks provided.

_____ 1. Keeping hands and feet apart when crawling on stairs allows firefighters to _____ if stairs collapse. (432)

A. brace
B. balance
C. hold on
D. catch themselves

_____ 2. What search method is used to conduct a primary search of large or complex areas filled with smoke? (435)

A. General search method
B. Oriented-search method
C. Wide-area-search method
D. Thermal-imager-search method

_____ 3. When marking searched rooms, a firefighter should NEVER: (438)

A. conduct the search systematically.
B. block the door open with furniture.
C. use latch straps to prevent doors from closing.
D. place the marks low enough to be seen under smoke.

_____ 4. When using the Federal Emergency Management Agency's Urban Search and Rescue marking system what is noted to the right of the X? (438)

A. Hazards

B. Search unit

C. Time of completion

D. Victims and condition

_____ 5. The "two-in, two-out" rule requires there are: (444)

A. two teams working inside the structure at all times.

B. two firefighters that switch places every two rotations.

C. two teams to conduct the primary and secondary search.

D. two firefighters outside the structure to rescue two firefighters working inside.

_____ 6. In the acronym LUNAR, the R stands for: (447)

A. radio.

B. request help.

C. resources needed.

D. required equipment.

_____ 7. Which of the following seeking safe haven actions should only be done as a last resort when it is too late to exit? (450)

A. Stay low to the floor

B. Use the hose stream for protection

C. Use tools to shore building material

D. Close doors between firefighter and fire

_____ 8. Which of the following BEST describes when escape is the best option for a firefighter? (450)

A. There are several places to seek safe shelter.

B. There is imminent threat of a structural collapse.

C. There is enough air in SCBA to continue search and still safely exit.

D. There are no immediate indications extreme fire conditions are about to occur.

_____ 9. When searching for an exit, use one hand to find the window and the other hand to sweep the floor ahead to avoid: (452)

A. openings.

B. occupants.

C. traps or dangerous objects.

D. objects obstructing the way.

_____ 10. In the rapid intervention crew or team acronym AWARE, the R stands for: (454)

A. a radio.

B. rapid team.

C. request help.

D. required equipment.

_____ 11. Which of the following may interfere with the efforts of the rapid intervention crew or team (RIC/RIT) when searching for a downed firefighter? (454)

A. Search line

B. Thermal imager

C. Forcible entry devices

D. Noise-producing devices on scene

_____ 12. The search mode of a tracking device used to locate lost or disoriented firefighters displays the distance and direction: (456)

A. toward all egress points.

B. away from the fire origin.

C. toward an egress transmitter positioned near an exit.

D. away from an egress transmitter positioned near an exit.

Short Answer

Write the correct answers on the blanks provided.

1. What three skills should a firefighter learn to ensure survival? (443)

____

____

____

2. What four actions should a firefighter take in preparation for survival? (444)

____

____

____

____

____

____

____

____

3. What information must a firefighter communicate in the event of a MAYDAY situation? (446)

____

____

____

4. What are the key principles of air management? (448)

____

____

____

Crossword Puzzle

Across

1. To operate independently of the Incident Commander's command and control
6. Slow, thorough search to ensure that no occupants were overlooked during the primary search
7. Striking the surface of a roof or floor to determine its structural integrity or locate underlying support members
8. Assessment of a facility or location made before an emergency occurs, in order to prepare for an appropriate emergency response
10. To reignite because of latent heat, sparks, or smoldering embers
11. Any facility in which a fire, accident, or natural disaster could cause substantial casualties or significant economic harm, through either property or infrastructure damage
12. Ongoing evaluation of influential factors at the scene of an incident

Down

2. Alarm that sounds when SCBA air supply is low, typically 25 percent
3. Point at which air in the SCBA will last only long enough to exit a hazardous atmosphere
4. Two or more firefighters designated to perform firefighter rescue; they are stationed outside the hazard and must be standing by throughout the incident
5. Internationally recognized distress signal
9. Rapid but thorough search to determine the location of victims; performed either before or during fire suppression operations

1
2
3
4
5
6
7
8
9
10
11

Chapter 10

Scene Lighting, Rescue Tools, Vehicle Extrication, and Technical Rescue

Firefighter I

Terms

Write the definition of the terms below on the blanks provided.

1. **Extrication (479)** ______________________________

____

2. **Generator (480)** ______________________________

____

3. **Power Take-Off (PTO) System (480)** ______________________________

____

4. **Inverter (481)** ______________________________

____

5. **Intrinsically Safe (483)** ______________________________

____

6. **Ground Fault Circuit Interrupter (GFCI) (484)** ______________________________

____

True/False

Write True or False on the blanks provided; if False, write the correct statement on the lines provided.

_______ 1. Electric generators are the most common power source used by emergency services personnel. (480)

____

____

_______ 2. Vehicle-mounted generators produce less power than portable units. (480)

_______ 3. Lighting equipment can be divided into three categories. (481)

_______ 4. Fixed lights are used to provide overall lighting of the emergency scene. (481)

_______ 5. All auxiliary electrical equipment must be waterproof, intrinsically safe, and designed for the amount of electrical current it is intended to carry. (483)

_______ 6. Junction boxes provide a connection supplied through multiple inlets from a power source. (484)

Identification

Write the correct answers on the blanks provided.

Lighting and Auxiliary Electrical Equipment (483-484)
Identify the piece of lighting and auxiliary electrical equipment in the images below.

1. ______________________________

2. ______________________________

3. ______________________________

4. ______________________________

5. ______________________________

6. ______________________________

Terms

Write the definition of the terms below on the blanks provided.

1. **Arc (484)** ____

2. **Stabilization (493)** ____

3. **Wheel Chock (495)** ____

4. **Cribbing (496)** ____

5. **Pretensioner (506)** ____

6. **B-Post (519)** ____

7. **Safety Glass (522)** ____

8. **Tempered Glass (522)** ____

9. **Nader Pin (526)** ____

10. **Unibody Construction (527)** ____

11. **Case-Hardened Steel (528)** ____________________

____

12. **Secondary Collapse (538)** ____________________

____

13. **Hypothermia (542)** ____________________

____

14. **Low-Head Dam (542)** ____________________

____

15. **Lockout/Tagout Device (545)** ____________________

____

16. **Ground Gradient (549)** ____________________

____

True/False

Write True or False on the blanks provided; if False, write the correct statement on the lines provided.

_______ 1. Electric rescue tools may be less powerful than those with other power sources. (487)

____

____

_______ 2. Most electric rescue tools are vehicle repair tools adapted to fire service use. (490)

____

____

_______ 3. Jacks should always be placed on a flat, level surface. (493)

____

____

_______ 4. Wheel chocks can hold a vehicle in place on a 20 to 25 percent grade. (495)

____

____

_______ 5. Synthetic fiber cable used for winches is not as strong as steel cable. (500)

____

____

_______ 6. Firefighters should only use recommended types of lubricants, hydraulic fluids, and fuel grades when performing maintenance on rescue tools. (503)

____

____

_______ 7. During vehicle extrication, it may be necessary to activate foam-generating systems and deploy several charged lines. (508)

____

____

_______ 8. A buttress tension system is used to stabilize vehicles that are upside down or lying on a side. (516)

____

____

_______ 9. Seat belt pretensioners lock before a crash to prevent further travel. (519)

____

____

_______ 10. Firefighters can use duct tape to form handles that will help carry or control broken glass. (526)

____

____

_______ 11. When removing a vehicle roof, always place a step chock under the A-post. (527)

____

____

_______ 12. The next priority after stabilizing the incident scene is to establish scene security. (533)

____

____

_______ 13. Confined space rescue operations may take place in a location that is designed for continuous occupancy. (538)

____

____

_______ 14. When at water rescue operations assisting technical teams, firefighters may wear structural PPE for warmth. (541)

____

____

_______ 15. During wilderness rescue operations in hot climates, wearing structural PPE for protection is recommended. (543)

____

____

_______ 16. The handrails and steps of an escalator move at different rates. (546)

____

____

Identification

Write the correct answers on the blanks provided.

Powered Rescue Tools (489-490)

Identify the powered rescue tool in the images below.

1. ______________________________

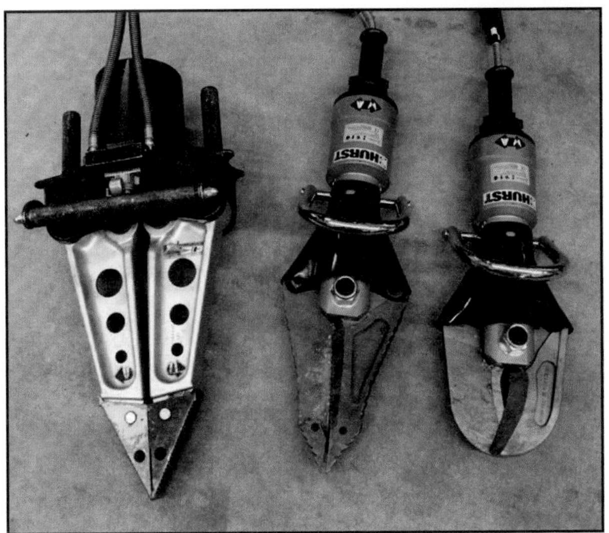

2. ______________________________

3. ______________________________

4. ______________________________

Structural Collapse Patterns (536-537)

Identify the structural collapse pattern in the images below.

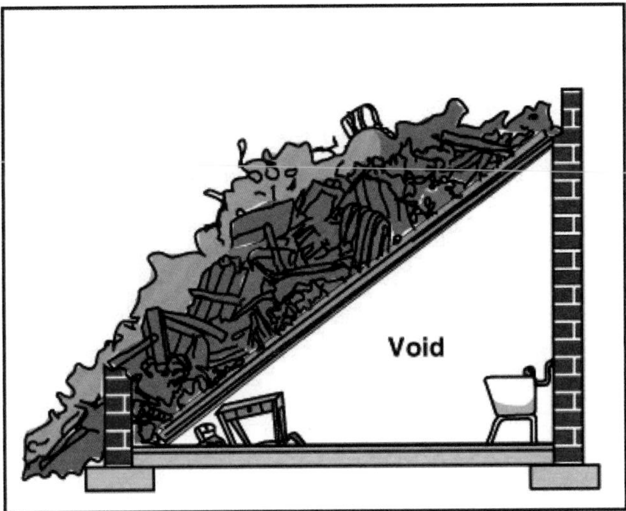

1. ______________________________

2. ______________________________

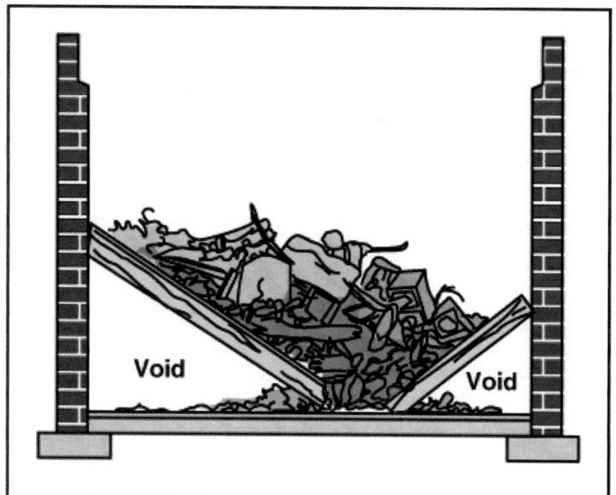

3. ____________________

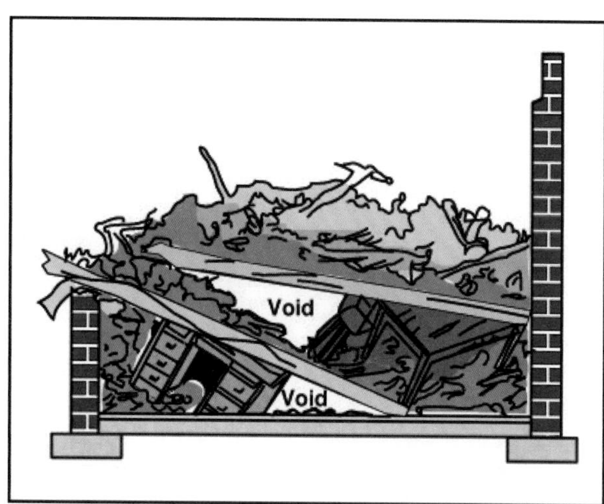

4. 

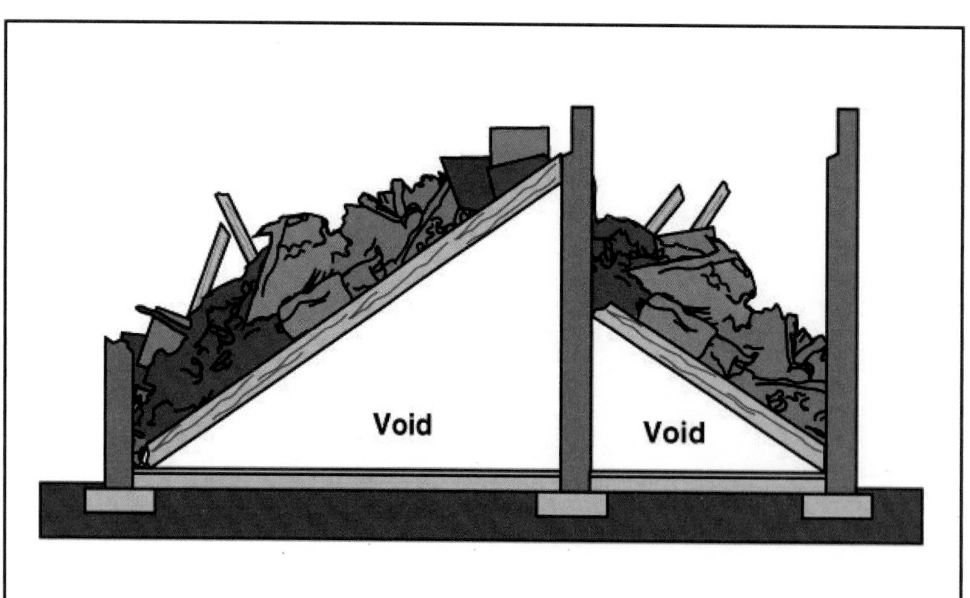

5. ____________________

Matching

Write the correct answers on the blanks provided.

Rescue Tool Uses

Match the definition with the rescue tool use listed. Each choice will be used once.

_______ 1. Ensuring that the vehicle or structural member will not move during rescue (486)

_______ 2. Dragging away materials to free a victim (486)

_______ 3. Removing materials or debris to free a victim (486)

_______ 4. Securing materials in place or breaking up materials to free a victim (486)

_______ 5. Raising vehicle, vehicle component, or structural member off victim or raising victim out of a space (486)

A. Cutting
B. Lifting
C. Pulling
D. Stabilizing
E. Other activities

Cutting Tools

Match the definition with the correct cutting tool listed. Each choice will be used once.

_______ 1. Tool that can have large-toothed blades used for rough cuts or fine-toothed blades for precision cuts (491)

_______ 2. Tool often used for delicate cutting operations (492)

_______ 3. Tool that operates at pressures between 90 and 250 psi (630 and 1 750 kPa) (492)

_______ 4. Tool that is versatile, lightweight, and is available in a battery-powered model (492)

_______ 5. Tool that has a short, straight blade that moves in and out (491)

A. Air chisel
B. Rotary saw
C. Circular saw
D. Whizzer saw
E. Reciprocating saw

Stabilizing Tools

Match the definition with the correct stabilizing tool listed. Each choice will be used once.

_______ 1. The least stable of this type of tool, also known as high-lift (494)

_______ 2. Designed for heavy lifting, used to tighten opposing members in shoring system (493)

_______ 3. Can hold a vehicle in place on a 10 to 15 percent grade (495)

_______ 4. Consists of wooden or plastic blocks of varying lengths (496)

_______ 5. Uses threaded stem component system to operate, primarily used to hold object in place (493)

_______ 6. Arrangement of at least three 4 x 4 (101 by 101 mm) posts wedged between the ground and vehicle (495)

_______ 7. Has two swivel footplates that adjust on a threaded system, replace wooden cross braces during rescue (494)

A. Wheel chocks
B. Hydraulic jack
C. Bar screw jack
D. Trench screw jack
E. Ratchet-lever jack
F. Cribbing materials
G. Buttress tension system

10

Multiple Choice

Write the correct answers on the blanks provided.

_____ 1. Which of the following should be consulted if a problem is found during routine maintenance of a generator? (484)

A. Supervisor
B. The internet
C. The manual
D. Division commander

_____ 2. Which of the following devices powers most powered rescue tools? (488)

A. Come-alongs
B. Manual power
C. Pneumatic power
D. Hydraulic pumps

_____ 3. What tool uses paint on the ends of blocks to indicate length? (496)

A. Wheel chocks
B. Cribbing material
C. Ratchet-lever jacks
D. Combination spreader/shears

_____ 4. Which of the following BEST describes a disadvantage of plastic cribbing? (496)

A. It is lighter and lasts longer.
B. It may slip under wet conditions.
C. It cannot be contaminated by absorbing oil or fuel.
D. It can be locally constructed or commercially purchased.

_____ 5. Which of the following BEST describes scene size-up during vehicle extrication? (504)

A. Size-up ends after firefighters arrive on scene.
B. Size-up helps identify potential hazards on scene.
C. Size-up begins only when firefighters arrive on scene.
D. Size-up is performed by the first arriving firefighter and then it ends.

_____ 6. Which of the following can be used to supplement chocks during vehicle stabilization? (514)

A. Impact tools
B. Come-alongs
C. Operable mechanical system in the vehicle
D. Inoperable mechanical system in the vehicle

_____ 7. Which of the following BEST describes a disadvantage of using a lifting jack? (515)
A. It is time-consuming to place.
B. It may be inserted into tight spaces.
C. It may deflate, causing vehicle to shift.
D. It can be adjusted to the required height.

_____ 8. Which of the following BEST describes a possible disadvantage for using pneumatic lifting bags? (515)
A. Bags are time-consuming to place.
B. Bags can be damaged or jarred loose.
C. Bags may be inserted into tight spaces.
D. Bags can be adjusted to the required height.

_____ 9. Which of the following BEST describes how to disconnect the electrical system in an electric vehicle? (518)
A. Just the same as in a conventional vehicle.
B. Use the disarming key code for the vehicle.
C. The opposite way as in a conventional vehicle.
D. There is no way to disconnect the electrical system.

_____ 10. Which of the following passenger safety systems can deploy even after the battery has been disconnected? (520)
A. Seat belt pretensioners
B. Head protection systems (HPS)
C. Extendable roll over protection systems (ROPS)
D. Supplemental passenger restraint systems (SPRS)

_____ 11. Which of the following passenger safety systems comes in two main types: window curtains and inflatable tubes? (521)
A. Seat belt pretensioners
B. Head protection systems (HPS)
C. Extendable roll over protection systems (ROPS)
D. Supplemental passenger restraint systems (SPRS)

_____ 12. Which of the following passenger safety systems will deploy if the vehicle becomes weightless for at least 80 milliseconds? (522)
A. Seat belt pretensioners
B. Head protection systems (HPS)
C. Extendable roll over protection systems (ROPS)
D. Supplemental passenger restraint systems (SPRS)

_____ 13. What method of gaining access to victims is used after a front-end collision when victims are pinned under the steering wheel? (528)

A. Removing the roof

B. Prying a door open

C. Removing a window

D. Displacing the dashboard

_____ 14. All emergency services personnel working the incident are able to access the: (534)

A. hot zone.

B. cold zone.

C. warm zone.

D. decontamination zone.

_____ 15. What type of structural collapse pattern occurs when one outer wall fails while the opposite wall remains intact? (538)

A. Pancake

B. Lean-to

C. V-shaped

D. Cantilever

_____ 16. When using the OATH method of communication during confined-space rescue, what does three tugs stand for? (540)

A. O – ok

B. H – help

C. A – advance

D. T – take-up slack

_____ 17. What type of device BEST fits the following characteristics: similar to freight, temporary installation? (545)

A. Escalator

B. Passenger elevator

C. Limited-use elevator

D. Construction elevator

_____ 18. What type of technical rescue involves physical hazards such as smoke, electrified rails, and standing water or other fluids? (548)

A. Cave rescue

B. Mine rescue

C. Tunnel rescue

D. Vehicle rescue

Short Answer

Write the correct answers on the blanks provided.

1. What are five of the questions that should be answered during size-up? (504)

 ____

 ____

 ____

 ____

 ____

2. What are the five hazards a firefighter must be aware of during vehicle extrication? (505)

 ____

 ____

 ____

 ____

 ____

3. What are the initial actions a Firefighter II can perform after reaching a technical rescue operation scene? (532)

 ____

 ____

 ____

 ____

 ____

Scenario

Read the scenario below, and then identify the lifting bag safety rules that were violated or not followed during the operation described.

Engine 127 and Rescue 127 are dispatched to a vehicle extrication incident involving a passenger vehicle that had left the roadway and collided with trees in a wooded area. After arriving on scene the crew finds a minivan with two patients trapped inside and one patient pinned under the vehicle. The ground around the vehicle is covered with sharp gravel and stones. Also present on the scene are several shattered tree limbs that fell to the ground during the collision.

The Incident Commander relays the command to begin extrication using pneumatic lifting bags immediately. Firefighter 1 begins the operation by placing a low-pressure lifting bag under the vehicle. A second low-pressure lifting bag is placed on top of this to make sure there is enough lifting distance provided. Firefighters 2 and 3 begin to air up the top bag while Firefighter 1 slowly slides under the vehicle to reach the patient underneath. While inflating the bag, Firefighters 2 and 3 discover that their equipment does not have enough air to properly inflate the bags needed to lift the vehicle.

Lifting bag safety rules violated:

____

____

____

____

____

____

____

____

Crossword Puzzle

Across

3. Block placed against the outer curve of a tire to prevent the apparatus from rolling
6. Wooden or plastic blocks used to stabilize a vehicle during vehicle extrication or debris following a structural collapse
7. Post between the front and rear doors on a four-door vehicle, or the door-handle-end post on a two-door car
10. Wall-like concrete structure across a river or stream that is designed to back up water
12. Method of automobile construction in which the frame and body form one integral unit
13. Electrical field that radiates outward from where the current enters the ground
14. Steel used in vehicle construction whose exterior has been heat treated, making it much harder than the interior metal
16. Treated glass that is stronger than plate glass or a single sheet of laminated glass; safer than regular glass because it crumbles into chunks when broken, instead of splintering into jagged shards

Down

1. Device used to secure a machine's power switches in order to prevent accidental re-start of the machine
2. Preventing unwanted movement; accomplished by supporting key places between an object and the ground (or other solid anchor points)
4. Collapse that occurs after the initial collapse of a structure
5. Device that takes up slack in a seat belt; prevents the passenger from being thrown forward in the event of a crash
8. Two sheets of glass laminated to a sheet of plastic sandwiched between them
9. Bolt on a vehicle's door frame that the door latches onto in order to close
11. High-temperature luminous electric discharge across a gap or through a medium such as charred insulation
15. Abnormally low body temperature

1
2
3
4
5
6
7
8
9
10
11
12
13
14
15
16

Chapter 11

Forcible Entry

Terms

Write the definition of the terms below on the blanks provided.

1. **Forcible Entry (573)** ____________________

2. **Lever (587)** ____________________

3. **Fulcrum (587)** ____________________

4. **Halligan Tool (587)** ____________________

5. **Adz (588)** ____________________

6. **Pike Pole (589)** ____________________

7. **Battering Ram (590)** ____________________

8. **Rabbit Tool (599)** ____________________

9. **Tempered Plate Glass (600)** ____________________

10. **Breaching (616)** ____________________

11

True/False

Write True or False on the blanks provided; if False, write the correct statement on the lines provided.

Firefighter I

_____ 1. If normal means of access is available, forcible entry should still be used. (574)

_____ 2. When a bolt protrudes from a lock into a receiver that is mortised into a jamb, it is in a locked position. (576)

_____ 3. Shutting off the power will not release an electromagnetic door. (580)

_____ 4. It is difficult to tell if locking devices are mounted prior to attempted entry. (581)

_____ 5. No single cutting tool will safely and efficiently cut all materials. (582)

_____ 6. Rebar cutters are only available in powered versions. (584)

_____ 7. Never use a power saw in a flammable atmosphere. (585)

_____ 8. The longer the handle on a prying tool, the lesser the force produced at the working end. (587)

_______ 9. Rambars have a sliding weight on a shaft that is used to drive a wedge or fork into an opening. (588)

_______ 10. Pike poles and hooks give firefighters a reach advantage when being used for pushing or pulling. (589)

_______ 11. A rotary saw is the only forcible entry tool that handles all situations. (591)

_______ 12. There is a sudden release of energy when a door, window, or wall is opened. (592)

_______ 13. You should push saws beyond design limitations only as a last resort. (592)

_______ 14. Dull saws are less likely to cause an accident. (592)

_______ 15. Carry a pick-head axe by covering the pick with a gloved hand. (593)

_______ 16. Pike poles should be carried ahead of the body when outside a structure. (593)

_______ 17. Soaking a handle in water can cause wood to swell. (594)

_______ 18. It is easier to drive a thick axe head through ordinary objects. (595)

_______ 19. Metal protectant that contains 1-1-1-trichloroethane can strengthen a handle. (595)

_______ 20. Minor damage is not a problem that causes potential harm in power equipment. (596)

_______ 21. Only the fire department possesses a master key that opens all lockboxes in a jurisdiction. (597)

_______ 22. Techniques for breaking door glass and window glass are similar. (598)

_______ 23. If you can see the hinges of a swinging door, it swings away from you. (599)

_______ 24. Hinges are mounted on the inside of outward-swinging doors. (600)

_______ 25. Weather molding must be removed from double doors when using a saw. (600)

_______ 26. High-security padlocks are designed with heel and toe shackles that will pivot if only one side of shackle is cut. (606)

_______ 27. Metal-frame windows are difficult to pry. (611)

____

____

_______ 28. Casement windows with one full pane do not require cranking once glass is removed. (611)

____

____

_______ 29. Lexan® is 500 times stronger than safety glass. (614)

____

____

_______ 30. When using a rotary saw to force entry, make vertical cuts first. (614)

____

____

_______ 31. Interior walls may be load-bearing or non-load-bearing. (619)

____

____

_______ 32. Carpets and rugs must be removed before cutting wooden floors. (620)

____

____

_______ 33. Fence material that is stretched tight can recoil when cut and cause injury. (621)

____

____

Identification

Identify the following items on the lines provided.

Types of Saws (584-586)

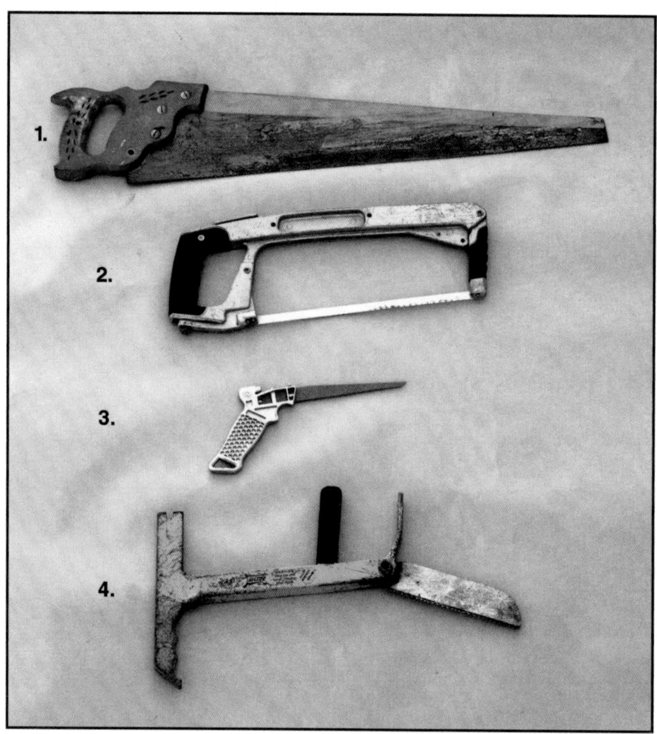

1. ______________________________

2. ______________________________

3. ______________________________

4. ______________________________

Types of Prying Tools (587-589)

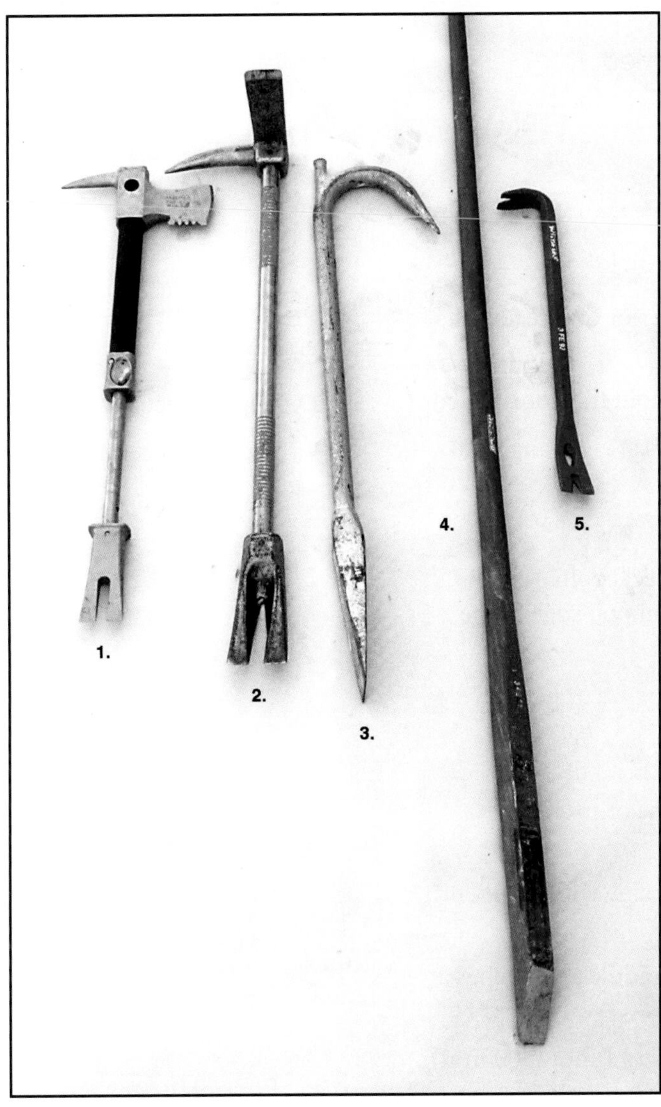

1. ______________________________

2. ______________________________

3. ______________________________

4. ______________________________

5. ______________________________

Firefighter I

Matching

Write the correct answers on the blanks provided.

Door Locks (575-580)
Match the type of lock with the description.

_______ 1. Most common type of lockset

_______ 2. Mounted into cavity in door edge

_______ 3. Electronic keyless lock found on exterior or interior doors

_______ 4. Older assemblies only have latch to hold the door closed

_______ 5. Installation involves boring two holes at right angles to one another

_______ 6. Mounted on interior door surface

_______ 7. Dead bolt lock that engages and projects bolts 1 inch (25.4 mm) into two or more points on one edge of the door

A. Mortise

B. Cylindrical

C. Rim

D. Higher Security

Windows (609-612)
Match the type of window with the description.

_______ 1. Constructed of a large solid glass pane or multiple panels

_______ 2. Constructed by being hinged on one side with wooden or metal frames

_______ 3. Constructed with hinge pins in the middle and latches at bottom of window

_______ 4. Constructed with large sections of glass 1 foot (300 mm) high

_______ 5. Constructed of small glass sections about 4 inches (100 mm) high and width of window

_______ 6. Constructed of metal sashes with a wire glass that pivots on hinges in the upper corners of a panel

_______ 7. Constructed of two glass or plastic sashes that are fitted at the top and bottom that slide up or down

A. Fixed

B. Double-hung

C. Casement

D. Awning

E. Jalousie

F. Projecting

G. Pivoting

Multiple Choice

Write the correct answers on the blanks provided.

_____ 1. Which of the following keeps doors closed? (575)

A. Locks
B. Hinges
C. Latches
D. Doorknobs

_____ 2. Which of the following are the two types of cylindrical locks? (576)

A. Multiple bolt and keyless entry
B. Night latch and vertical dead bolt
C. Key-in-knob and tubular dead bolt
D. Electromagnetic and electronic dead bolt

_____ 3. Which of the following is a dead bolt lock that engages and projects bolts 1 inch (25 mm) into two or more points on one edge of the door? (579)

A. Multiple bolt lock
B. Single cylinder lock
C. Double cylinder lock
D. Mortise latch or lock

_____ 4. Which of the following permits a door to be opened wide enough to see and speak to a visitor but restrict access? (580)

A. Drop bar
B. Door chain
C. Door limiter
D. Surface bolt

_____ 5. Which of the following should be available when using a rotary saw? (586)

A. Fuel
B. Spare blade
C. Charged hoseline
D. Replacement spark plug

_____ 6. A hydraulic ram can spread from: (588)

A. 10 to 16 inches (254 mm to 406 mm).
B. 20 to 26 inches (508 mm to 660 mm).
C. 36 to 63 inches (900 mm to 1 600 mm).
D. 40 to 46 inches (1 016 mm to 1 168 mm).

_____ 7. Which of the following has two knifelike wings that depress as the tool head is driven through a wall? (589)

A. Iron

B. Plaster hook

C. Shove knife

D. Bam-bam tool

_____ 8. What is the twisting caused by a spinning saw blade called? (593)

A. Torque

B. Vertical rotation

C. Horizontal vibration

D. Gyroscopic or torsion effect

_____ 9. How should a pike pole or hook BEST be carried? (593)

A. Behind the body

B. Away from body

C. Over the shoulder

D. Low to the ground

_____ 10. Which of the following should be addressed during care and maintenance of a wooden handle entry tool? (594)

A. Preserve it with paint

B. Preserve it with varnish

C. Check tightness of head

D. Check the weight of head

_____ 11. Which the following handles are easily maintained? (595)

A. Metal

B. Plated

C. Wooden

D. Fiberglass

_____ 12. Which of the following is protected by chromium or other metals applied during the electroplating process? (595)

A. Power tools

B. Plated surfaces

C. Fiberglass handles

D. Unprotected metal surfaces

_____ 13. Which of the following is the BEST method for caring for an unprotected metal surface? (595)
   A. Apply oil to striking surface of tool
   B. Wash with mild detergent and water
   C. Use mechanical grinder to sharpen blades
   D. Use metal file to remove burrs from cutting edge

_____ 14. Damage can be justified by ___ and speed needed for entry. (597)
   A. cost of repairs
   B. personnel available
   C. efficiency of entry
   D. severity of emergency

_____ 15. Which of the following are also known as flush fitting doors? (600)
   A. Double swinging doors
   B. Inward-swinging doors
   C. Outward-swinging doors
   D. Internal-mounted bolt doors

_____ 16. Which of the following is MOST accurate about tempered plate glass doors? (600)
   A. They are easy to break.
   B. They are lightweight.
   C. They are not breakable.
   D. They are heat resistant.

_____ 17. Which of the following is a type of sliding door? (602)
   A. Hidden door
   B. High-security
   C. Automatic door
   D. Interior pocket door

_____ 18. Which of the following would be BEST to use to force entry on a security gate? (602)
   A. Break lock with an axe.
   B. Break hinges with rambar.
   C. Strike bottom corner with pick-head axe.
   D. Cut an opening near lock with rotary saw.

_____ 19. Which of the following was designed to fit through a space between double-swinging doors equipped with panic hardware? (604)
   A. A-tool
   B. J-tool
   C. Key hole saw
   D. Shove knife tool

_____ 20. How large should the opening be when using a rotary saw to force overhead doors? (606)

A. 2 feet (0.6 m)

B. 4 feet (1.2 m)

C. 6 feet (2 m)

D. 8 feet (2.4 m)

_____ 21. Which of the following is MOST accurate about breaking window glass? (609)

A. It can reduce fire spread.

B. The glass can further injure victims.

C. It provides faster entry to structure.

D. The shards provide more traction for walking on.

_____ 22. Which of the following types of windows can contain wire glass or acrylic plastic? (611)

A. Awning

B. Jalousie

C. Casement

D. Double-hung

_____ 23. Which of the following consists of metal grates that are secured to the exterior of window openings? (615)

A. Strongbacks

B. High-security windows

C. Security bars and grilles

D. Vacant protection systems (VPS)

_____ 24. Which of the following are used to cut bars and grille frames? (616)

A. Axe

B. Handsaw

C. Chain saw

D. Rebar cutter

_____ 25. Which of the following is breached by using a chain saw equipped with a diamond-tipped chain? (618)

A. Dry walls

B. Metal walls

C. Wooden walls

D. Concrete walls

_____ 26. The opening when forcing a metal wall should be at least: (619)

A. 2 feet (0.6 m).
B. 4 feet (1.2 m).
C. 6 feet (1.8 m).
D. 8 feet (2.4 m).

_____ 27. Which of the following is needed to breach a gypsum Lexan® wall? (619)

A. Axe
B. Handsaw
C. Power saw
D. Shove knife

_____ 28. Through-the-lock and rim lock technique would be used to gain access to: (622-623)

A. gates.
B. walls.
C. floors.
D. windows.

Short Answer

Write the correct answers on the lines provided.

1. What does a supervisor or Incident Commander consider when performing forcible entry? (574)

____

____

____

____

____

____

2. What are the three basic types of locks? (575)

____

____

____

3. What factors influence types of tool combinations? (591)

4. List four ways to prevent injury when using tools. (591-592)

5. What are the two options for cutting around a lock of a resisting inward swinging door? (599)

6. What three components should a firefighter understand when breaching walls? (616)

Crossword Puzzle

Across

4 Prying tool with a claw at one end and a spike or point at a right angle to a wedge at the other end

6 Solid steel bar with handles and guards, a fork on one end, and a blunt end on the other, used to break down doors or create holes in walls

8 Device consisting of a bar turning about a fixed point (fulcrum), using power or force applied at a second point to lift or sustain an object at a third point

9 Techniques used by fire personnel to gain entry into buildings, vehicles, aircraft, or other areas of confinement when normal means of entry are locked or blocked

10 A wedge-shaped blade attached at right angles to the handle of the tool

Down

1 Sharp prong and hook of steel, on a wood, metal, fiberglass, or plastic handle of varying length, used for pulling, dragging, and probing

2 Support or point of support on which a lever turns in raising or moving something

3 Hydraulic spreading tool that is specially designed to open doors that swing inward

5 Type of glass specially treated to become harder and more break-resistant than plate glass or a single sheet of laminated glass

7 The act of creating a hole in a wall or floor to gain access to a structure or portion of a structure

Chapter 12

Ground Ladders

Firefighter I

Terms

Write the definition of the terms below on the blanks provided.

1. **Heat Sensor Label (659)** ______________________________

2. **Single Ladder (660)** ______________________________

3. **Roof Ladder (661)** ______________________________

4. **Folding Ladder (661)** ______________________________

5. **Extension Ladder (661)** ______________________________

6. **Combination Ladder (661)** ______________________________

7. **Bedded Position (665)** ______________________________

8. **Rope Hose Tool (685)** ______________________________

True/False

Write True or False on the blanks provided; if False, write the correct statement on the lines provided.

_______ 1. NFPA® 1931 contains requirements for use, care, maintenance, and service testing of fire department ground ladders. (654-655)

_______ 2. Heat-treated aluminum ladders are also heat-resistant. (658)

_______ 3. NFPA® 1932 requires ladders be inspected after each use and on a monthly basis. (663)

_______ 4. The halyard cable should be taut when an extension ladder is in the bedded position. (665)

_______ 5. Ladders needing repair should be repaired by firefighters as part of their routine duties. (666)

_______ 6. A ladder's reach is the same as the ladder's designated length. (668)

_______ 7. One firefighter should be able to remove a ladder from an aerial apparatus. (670)

_______ 8. The desired angle of inclination formed by the ladder and the ground is 45 degrees. (677)

_______ 9. An easy way to determine the proper distance between the butt and the building is to divide the working length of the ladder by 10. (677)

____

____

_______ 10. A ladder must be placed flat on the ground prior to raising. (678)

____

____

_______ 11. The transition from carrying position to raise can and should take place in one smooth, continuous motion. (678)

____

____

_______ 12. A firefighter deploys a roof ladder after carrying it up an extension ladder that is resting against the building. (682)

____

____

_______ 13. Ground ladders must be secured whenever firefighters are climbing or working from the ladder. (684)

____

____

_______ 14. Whenever possible, tools should be carried up a ladder rather than hoisted with a utility rope. (686)

____

____

Identification

Parts of a Ladder (655-657)
Identify the following parts of a ladder on the lines provided.

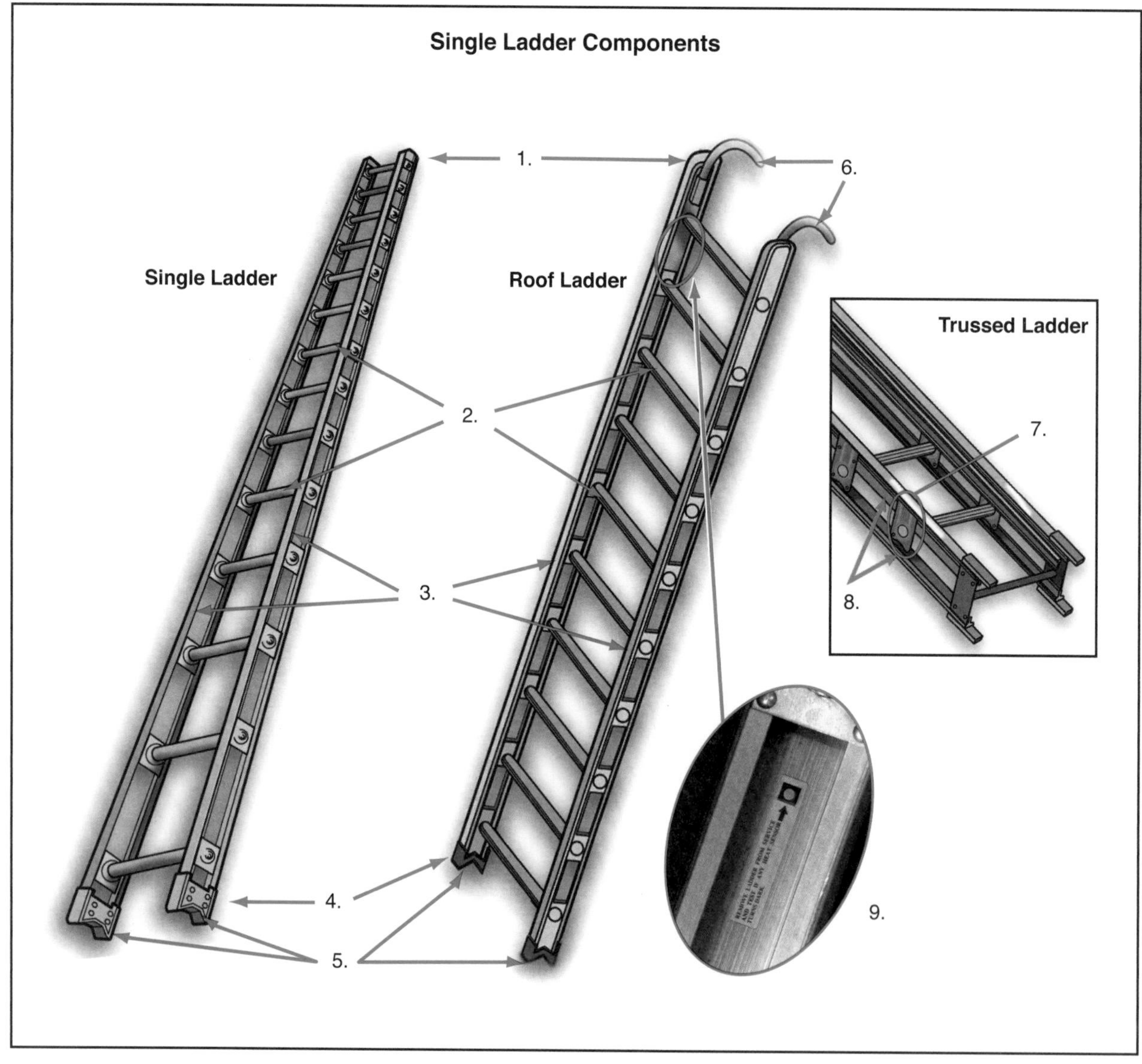

1. ____________________

2. ____________________

3. ____________________

4. ____________________

5. ____________________

6. ____________________

7. ____________________

8. ____________________

9. ____________________

Ladder Carries (670-675)
Identify the ladder carry pictured on the lines provided.

1. ____

2. ____

3. ____

4. ____

5. ____

Matching

Write the correct answers on the blanks provided.

Parts of an Extension Ladder

Match the description with the ladder part. Each choice will be used once.

_______ 1. Extreme top of a ladder (657)

_______ 2. Swivel plates attached to butt of the ladder (657)

_______ 3. Upper section of extension ladders; the section that moves (657)

_______ 4. Bottom end of the ladder, end that is placed on ground or supporting surface (657)

_______ 5. Small, grooved wheel through which the halyard is drawn on extension ladder (657)

_______ 6. Wooden or metal pieces that prevent the fly section from being extended too far (657)

_______ 7. Rope or cable used for hoisting and lowering fly sections of an extension ladder (657)

_______ 8. Wood or metal strips, slots, or channels on an extension ladder that guide the fly section (657)

_______ 9. Strips of metal attached at chafing points or at areas in contact with apparatus mounting brackets (657)

_______ 10. Devices attached to inside of beams on fly sections to hold the fly section in place after it has been extended (657)

_______ 11. Lowest, widest section of extension ladder that always maintains contact with the ground or supporting surface (655)

A. Bed section (base section, main section)
B. Butt (heel, base)
C. Fly section
D. Footpads (shoes)
E. Guides
F. Halyard (fly rope)
G. Pawls (dogs, ladder locks)
H. Protection plates
I. Pulley
J. Stops
K. Tip (top)

Ladder Types

Match the description with the ladder type. Each choice may be used more than once.

_____ 1. One section, nonadjustable (660)

_____ 2. Hinged rungs allow ladder to be folded (661)

_____ 3. Also called wall ladder, straight ladder (660)

_____ 4. Can be adjusted to specific length needed (661)

_____ 5. Distributes firefighter's weight while working (661)

_____ 6. Consists of base section with one or more fly sections (661)

_____ 7. Equipped with folding hooks that anchor ladder in place (661)

_____ 8. Can be carried in narrow passageways, used in attic scuttle holes or closets (661)

_____ 9. Must be equipped with positive locking devices to hold ladder in open position (661)

_____ 10. Designed to be used as self-supporting step-ladder and as single or extension ladder (661)

A. Single Ladder
B. Roof Ladder
C. Folding Ladder
D. Extension Ladder
E. Combination Ladder

Multiple Choice

Write the correct answers on the blanks provided.

_____ 1. Which of the following ladder markings is required by NFPA® 1931? (659)

A. Tip marked with white paint or reflective tape
B. Manufacturer's name plate with month and year of manufacture
C. Stripe indicating balance point of ladders under 24 feet (7 m)
D. Manufacturer's plate with material specifications and construction type

_____ 2. NFPA® 1901 requires aerial apparatus to carry one folding ladder, two single ladders equipped with roof hooks, and: (663)

A. one folding ladder.
B. two extension ladders.
C. one combination ladder.
D. one trussed straight ladder.

_____ 3. Darkening, blistering or blackening of varnish on wood ladders may indicate: (664)

A. exposure to heat.
B. exposure to water.
C. warping or twisting.
D. rust or damage to welds.

_____ 4. Which of the following is the BEST method of cleaning ground ladders? (666)

A. Pressure washer and alkaline detergent

B. Soft bristle brush, running water, and mild soap

C. Soft cloth and hydrocarbon solvent, such as kerosene

D. Commercial car wash, for ladders mounted on a ladder rack

_____ 5. Which of the following should be worn when training on ladders? (666)

A. PASS device

B. Full body harness with safety line

C. Personal flotation device and throw line

D. Supplied-air respirator with 30-minute supply

_____ 6. When lifting ladders below the waist, firefighters should use: (666)

A. leg muscles.

B. back muscles.

C. arm and chest muscles.

D. back and upper body muscles.

_____ 7. Ladders should not be raised within ___ of electrical wires. (666)

A. 3 feet (1 m)

B. 10 feet (3 m)

C. 24 feet (7 m)

D. 100 feet (30 m)

_____ 8. Grasp extension ladder ___ when raising or lowering to prevent fingers from being pinched or caught between ladder sections. (667)

A. rungs

B. pawls

C. beams

D. halyard

_____ 9. To prevent overloading, never load a ladder with more than: (667)

A. one firefighter per ladder.

B. one firefighter per ten feet (3 m).

C. two firefighters per extension ladder section.

D. two firefighters per ten feet (3 m) of working length.

_____ 10. When a team is lifting a ladder, the command to lift is given by: (669)

A. the Incident Commander.

B. the most senior firefighter on the team.

C. the firefighter who will be first to climb the ladder.

D. the firefighter who can see other members of the team.

_____ 11. When carrying a roof ladder to deploy on a roof, the roof hooks are opened: (675)

A. when the ladder is removed from the apparatus.

B. when the tip of the ladder has reached the tip of the roof.

C. when the ladder is heeled at the base of the extension ladder.

D. when the ladder has been carried to the top of the extension ladder.

_____ 12. What is the proper position for a ladder being used by a firefighter who will break a window for ventilation? (675)

A. Alongside the window on the upwind side

B. With the ladder tip placed slightly below the sill

C. Directly in front of the window, tip on wall above window

D. Adjacent to the window, with three or four rungs above the roofline

_____ 13. Place the ladder with the tip slightly below the sill if the ladder is to be used for: (676)

A. supporting a smoke ejector.

B. performing entry or rescue from a window.

C. breaking a window for ventilation.

D. directing a hose stream into a narrow window.

_____ 14. If a ladder comes to rest a safe distance from electrical lines but passes within 10 feet (3 m) of the electrical lines during raising, firefighters may: (678)

A. access that portion of the structure from an internal stairway.

B. be required to use an alternative method of raising the ladder.

C. use only aerial apparatus to access that portion of the structure.

D. access that portion of the structure from above using a roof ladder.

_____ 15. What is the correct position of the fly on an extension ladder? (679)

A. In, toward the structure

B. Out, away from the structure

C. Position specified by manufacturer

D. Position determined by firefighter placing ladder butt

_____ 16. How is the halyard secured before climbing an extension ladder? (679)

A. Held securely by the firefighter heeling in the ladder
B. Tied to the ladder with a rope hose tool or safety strap
C. Attached with a carabiner to the ladder belt or safety harness
D. Tied to the ladder with a clove hitch and overhand safety knot

_____ 17. How can a single firefighter raising an extension ladder prevent the butt of the ladder from slipping while the ladder is brought to the vertical position? (680)

A. Tie in the ladder before raising
B. Engage the pawls before raising
C. Heel the butt against the building
D. Heel the butt against the apparatus

_____ 18. When two or more firefighters are raising a ladder, who is responsible for placing the butt at the desired position and giving commands during the operation? (680)

A. Incident Commander
B. Most senior firefighter
C. Firefighter positioned at the tip
D. Firefighter positioned at the butt

_____ 19. Two methods for securing ground ladders are: (684)

A. heeling and tying in.
B. pivoting and shifting.
C. deploying and racking.
D. tying the halyard and tying a safety.

_____ 20. Which of the following BEST describes the proper position for climbing a ladder? (685)

A. Arms bent at 45-degree angle, hands grasping rails
B. Arms straight (horizontal), hands grasping rungs palms down
C. Arms bent at 45-degree angle, hands grasping rungs palms up
D. Arms straight, two rungs distance above head, hands grasping rails

_____ 21. Which of the following statements BEST describes the method of lowering a conscious victim down a ladder? (687)

A. Victim is lowered feet first, facing the building
B. Victim is lowered feet first, facing the firefighter
C. Victim's feet are placed outside rails to avoid entanglement
D. Victim is lowered with escape rope and ladder belt around waist

Short Answer

Write the correct answers on the lines provided.

1. List three advantages of metal ladders. (658)

____

____

____

2. List three advantages of wooden ladders. (658)

____

____

____

3. What are two disadvantages of fiberglass ladders? (658)

____

____

4. According to NFPA® 1901, what ladders are required to be carried on pumper apparatus? (661)

____

____

____

5. What are five elements to be inspected on all ladders? (663)

____

____

____

____

____

6. When are three occasions that ground ladders should be service tested? (665)

____

____

____

7. What are five factors to consider when deciding where to place a ladder? (667-668)

8. List five things firefighters must know to assist them in using ground ladders mounted on apparatus. (671)

9. What are three situations to avoid when placing ladders? (676-677)

10. List three benefits of a 75-degree climbing angle. (677)

11. What are two situations when a ladder may have to be pivoted or shifted after raising? (683)

12. Name two ways to safely secure a firefighter to a ladder while performing work. (686)

Crossword Puzzle

Across

3. Extension ladder with the fly section(s) fully retracted
6. Variable-length ladder of two or more sections that can be extended to a desired height
7. Single-section, collapsible ladder that is easy to maneuver in restricted places such as access openings for attics and lofts
8. Piece of rope spliced to form a loop through the eye of a metal hook; used to secure hose to ladders or other objects

Down

1. One-section nonadjustable ladder
2. Ladder that can be used as a single, extension, or A-frame ladder
4. Straight ladder with folding hooks at the top end
5. Label affixed to the ladder beam near the tip to provide a warning that the ladder has been subjected to excessive heat

Chapter 13

Tactical Ventilation

Terms

Write the definition of the terms below on the blanks provided.

1. **Air Flow (737)** ______________________________

2. **Blowers (742)** ______________________________

3. **Smoke Ejectors (742)** ______________________________

4. **Horizontal Ventilation (742)** ______________________________

5. **Vertical Ventilation (742)** ______________________________

6. **Natural Ventilation (743)** ______________________________

7. **Mechanical Ventilation (743)** ______________________________

8. **Hydraulic Ventilation (743)** ______________________________

9. **Leeward Side (745)** ______________________________

10. **Windward Side (745)** ______________________________

11. **Exhaust Opening (745)** ______________________________

12. **Negative-Pressure Ventilation (NPV) (745)** ______________________________

13. **Recirculation (746)** ______________________________

14. **Positive-Pressure Ventilation (PPV) (746)** ______________________________

15. **Kerf Cut (756)** ______________________________

16. **Louver Cut or Vent (757)** ______________________________

17. **Trench Ventilation (758)** ______________________________

18. **Stack Effect (761)** ______________________________

19. **Horizontal Smoke Spread (762)** ______________________________

True/False

Write True or False on the blanks provided; if False, write the correct statement on the lines provided.

_______ 1. Tactical ventilation is the coordinated removal of heated air, smoke, and gases from a structure. (732)

____

____

_______ 2. Performing tactical ventilation properly increases the potential for extreme fire behavior. (733)

____

____

_______ 3. Life safety is the highest incident priority at incidents where tactical ventilation is used. (733)

____

____

_______ 4. Tactical ventilation improves life safety for firefighters by creating smoke-free paths of egress. (733)

____

____

_______ 5. Tactical ventilation can be combined with fire attack to stabilize an incident. (733)

____

____

_______ 6. Smaller lot size reduces firefighter access and increases potential exposure risks. (735)

____

____

_______ 7. Fire attack crews with charged hoselines must be in place before orders are given to ventilate a structure. (739)

____

____

_______ 8. Atmospheric pressure is the most important weather condition influence when ventilating a structure. (740)

_______ 9. Positive-pressure ventilation (PPV) is the oldest type of mechanical ventilation. (745)

_______ 10. The flow of smoke and other gases to the exhaust opening should be kept as straight as possible. (746)

_______ 11. A trench cut is used to create a fire break to stop fire spread in common attic areas. (758)

_______ 12. Fire, smoke, and toxic gases can spread rapidly through pipe shafts, stairways, elevator shafts, unprotected ducts, and other vertical or horizontal openings in a big box store fire. (761)

Fill in the Blank

Write the correct answer on the blanks provided.

1. Firefighters protect both occupants and personnel working at an incident scene. The highest priority is _______________. (733)

2. During tactical ventilation firefighters work to control and extinguish the fire in stages. By combining tactical ventilation with fire attack, firefighters reach the incident priority of ____________. (733)

3. Properly applied, tactical ventilation can reduce fire damage in a structure. Tactical ventilation can confine fire to a specific area. Both of these are examples of the incident priority of______________. (733-734)

4. When the pressure is higher inside a building, smoke can be forced through openings to the lower-pressure area outside. The technique of using high-volume fans to create the slightly higher pressure inside the structure than outside is _______________. (746)

5. Firefighters choose ventilation methods based on many factors. When your Incident Commander gives orders for ventilation by making an opening over the seat of the fire at or near the highest point of the roof, he or she is ordering you to perform ______________. (756)

6. An Incident Commander may determine a fire is too great to extinguish and will make the call to abandon efforts to save the building. Only after offensive vertical ventilation openings have been made, the Incident Commander may give you orders to perform ________________ to allow heat and smoke to escape. (758)

Matching

Write the correct answers on the blanks provided.

Fire Behavior Indicators

Match what the fire behavior indicator shows with the indicators listed. Each choice will be used once.

_________ 1. If visible, this indicator provides an indication of the size and location of the fire. (738)

_________ 2. Blistering paint, bubbling roofing tar, and crazed glass are visual indicators of this fire behavior. (738)

_________ 3. Volume and location of discharge, color, density, pressure and movement of this indicator can help firefighters obtain a clear picture of interior fire conditions. (737)

_________ 4. Indicators of this fire behavior indicator include velocity, turbulence, direction, and movement of the neutral plane. (737)

A. Smoke

B. Air Flow

C. Heat

D. Flame

Types and Methods of Ventilation

Match the type or method of ventilation with the methods provided. Each choice will be used once.

_____ 1. Using smoke ejectors to expel (pull) smoke from a structure by developing an artificial air flow or enhancing natural ventilation (745)

_____ 2. Used to clear the room or structure of smoke, heat, steam, or gases after the fire is controlled using a spray stream from a fog nozzle (744)

_____ 3. Using a high-volume fan to create a slightly higher pressure inside the structure than outside is done by using this type or method of ventilation (746)

_____ 4. Used when the natural flow of air currents and currents created by the fire are insufficient to remove the smoke, heat, and fire gases (745)

_____ 5. Using only a single opening where the vent will serve as both the inlet for air and exit for the smoke (745)

_____ 6. Used when the decision is made to abandon efforts to save the currently burning part of the building (758)

_____ 7. Used to stop the spread of the fire and contain it in one area of the structure (752)

_____ 8. Used as an aid in reaching and extinguishing a fire (752)

A. Vertical ventilation
B. Defensive ventilation
C. Hydraulic ventilation
D. Offensive ventilation
E. Positive-pressure ventilation
F. Negative-pressure ventilation
G. Natural horizontal ventilation
H. Mechanical horizontal ventilation

Multiple Choice

Write the correct answers on the blanks provided.

_____ 1. Which of the following is NOT one of the three main incident priorities? (733)
A. Life safety
B. Water conservation
C. Incident stabilization
D. Property conservation

_____ 2. Which internal exposure must be considered when initiating tactical ventilation operations? (741)
A. Building occupants
B. Adjacent structures
C. Lowest point of building
D. Highest point of building

_____ 3. Identifying buildings that have roofs supported by lightweight or engineered trusses can be done by: (754)

A. using preincident planning information.

B. observing smoke emitting from roof in fire.

C. sounding all roofs located in fire response area.

D. coordinating the response team's visual inspection efforts.

_____ 4. Heating, ventilating, and air conditioning (HVAC) systems in windowless buildings, unless specifically designed to clear the area of smoke, are more likely to: (761)

A. contain products of combustion.

B. cause the spread of heat and fire.

C. force sprinkler systems to engage.

D. reduce potential extreme fire behavior.

_____ 5. Openings such as pipe shafts, stairways, elevator shafts, or unprotected ducts in a high-rise building fire contribute to what effect? (761)

A. Stack

B. Safety

C. Smoke

D. System

_____ 6. The number of personnel required for high-rise structure fires are often how much greater than typical low-rise structure incidents? (761)

A. Zero to two times

B. Two to four times

C. Four to six times

D. Six to eight times

_____ 7. Which of the following must be controlled in a high-rise structure fire to protect occupants from entering the ventilation stairwell as they evacuate? (762)

A. Elevators

B. HVAC system

C. Doors leading to the roof

D. Doors on uninvolved floors

_____ 8. Tactical ventilation usually must be accomplished using what type of tactical ventilation in a high-rise structure fire? (762)

A. Natural

B. Vertical

C. Hydraulic

D. Mechanical

_____ 9. Which of the following is a method of compartmentalizing a structure? (763)
A. Automatic activation of fire alarm
B. Automatic closure of doors and windows
C. Automatic evacuation of building occupants
D. Automatic opening of HVAC system operations

Short Answer

Write the correct answers on the blanks provided.

1. Fire can be confined to a specific area when four factors are removed from a burning structure. Name two of those factors. (732)

____

____

____

____

2. List at least four general reasons for performing tactical ventilation. (733)

____

____

____

____

3. List at least four factors that have a bearing on where to ventilate a structure. (740)

____

____

____

____

4. Describe the two main types of tactical ventilation. (742)

5. List five of the safety precautions firefighters need to take when performing vertical ventilation. (752-754)

6. Describe a kerf cut and a triangle cut. (756)

Scenario

Read the scenarios below and answer the following questions based on each scenario.

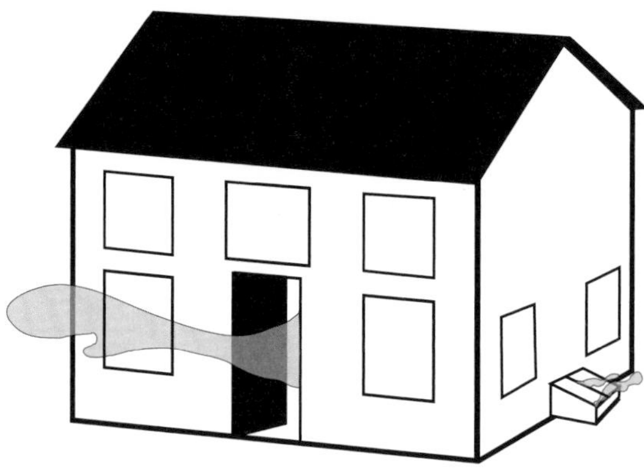

Scenario 1

You arrive on scene to a two-story single family residence with light smoke coming from the open front door on side A. Upon arrival, residents state that a fire started in the basement while doing some plumbing work. A 360° size up reveals a closed cellar door on side D with wispy smoke coming from the cracks.

1. What ventilation strategy does the presence of the cellar door allow?

____

____

____

____

2. What considerations will need to be examined before attempting to knock down the fire from the outside of the structure prior to making entry?

____

____

____

____

3. What could the light and wispy smoke from the cellar door indicate?

____

____

____

____

4. What offensive ventilation technique can help remove smoke from the first floor of the residence?

Scenario 2

You arrive at the scene of a fire in a four-story hotel. The manager informs you that the fire is in Room 312 which your pre-fire plan shows to be on the C-side of the hotel. Smoke is coming from a window on the third floor in the center of that side. No fire is visible and no apparent vertical extension of the fire is evident on the building exterior.

1. What is the first thing the Incident Commander should confirm about the fire upon arrival?

2. Once the fire is confirmed to be contained to one room, what should happen to the doors on the third floor?

3. Firefighters must remember that upon entering the room, the open doorway would have what effect?

4. Since there is a fourth floor above the fire, what type of ventilation must be utilized?

5. Prior to fire control teams entering the room from the hallway, which part of the third floor window should be broken to allow smoke to escape?

6. Once the room window is opened for ventilation, windows in the hallway may be opened. What piece of equipment would be positioned in the hallway to draw air from the windows to the fire room to force smoke and unburned fire gases out the room window?

7. If an aerial apparatus is positioned to allow firefighters to access the window outside the fire room on the upwind side of the window, what should they prepare for through the opened windows?

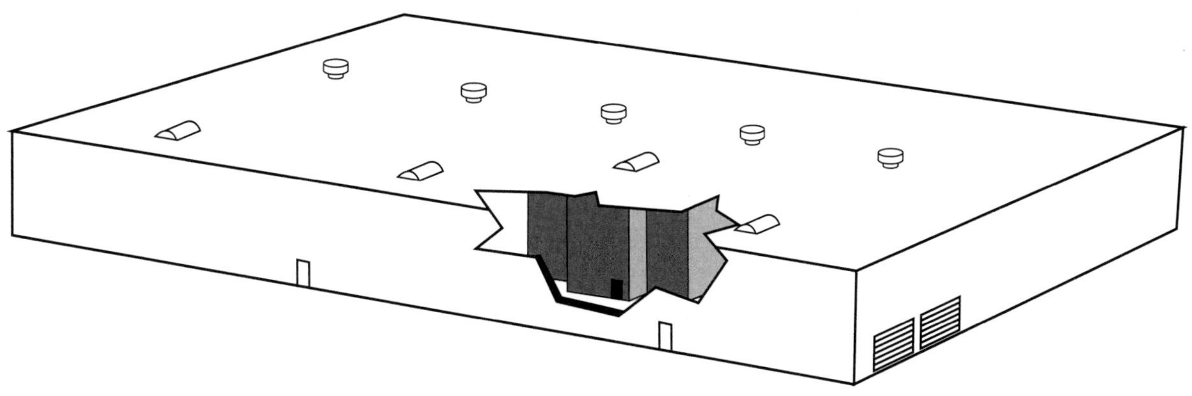

Scenario 3

You arrive at the scene of a fire in a big box store. Upon arrival, the store manager informs you that the fire has been confined to a large training room by the block walls on all four sides of the room and its fire-rated doors. This room is located within the structure between the back stock area and the public areas of the store. The room can be reached through a personnel door on the C-side of the structure or roll-up doors on the B-side of the structure. Entrance to the room is through an employee locker and break room which has helped trap the smoke and fire gases within the room of origin. Information from the manager and your 360° size-up reveals that there are a series of skylights and vents on the roof of the structure.

1. Based on the fact that the smoke is confined to a single room with block walls and fire-rated doors, to prevent smoke and gas spread to other parts of the store, what type of ventilation should be the priority?

____

____

____

____

2. The roof should be laddered in at least how many locations and for what two reasons?

____

____

____

____

3. What equipment should firefighters going onto the roof take with them?

____

____

____

____

4. Why should firefighters sound the roof as they near the area above the fire?

5. What should firefighters with roof handlines monitor for?

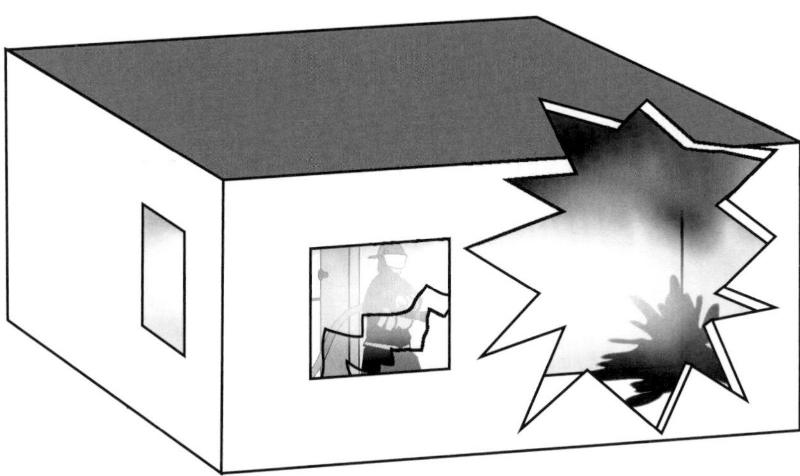

Scenario 4

You are dispatched in reference to a residential structure fire. Upon arrival you are met by the property owner who states that all occupants are out of the structure and that there is a fire in the back bedroom. As you are preparing to make entry, the truck company on scene ventilates the back bedroom window. Your crew makes entry with a 1 ¾" hoseline and due to light smoke conditions proceeds quickly to the rear of the structure. You find that the fire is still contained to the room of origin and it is quickly knocked down. However, there is a large amount of smoke and steam from the suppression effort.

1. What type of ventilation should be used in this situation? Why?

2. What should be the first concern after establishing there are no victims? There has been little fire spread and the fire is quickly controlled.

___

___

___

___

3. What result of the suppression effort should be immediately removed to prevent further damage to the structure's contents?

___

___

___

___

4. Based on the fact that the back bedroom window has been ventilated, what type of ventilation is a good option to quickly remove much of the smoke?

___

___

___

___

5. What considerations could make positive-pressure ventilation the less desirable type of ventilation in this situation?

___

___

___

___

Crossword Puzzle

Across

1. Tendency of heat, smoke, and other products of combustion to rise until they encounter a horizontal obstruction
7. Techniques that use the wind, convection currents, and other natural phenomena to ventilate a structure without the use of fans, blowers, and smoke ejectors
9. Protected side; the direction opposite from which the wind is blowing
13. Electrically powered fans that have intrinsically safe motors that are placed in the smoke-filled atmosphere to push the smoke out
16. Defensive tactic that involves cutting an exhaust opening in the roof of a burning building, extending from one outside wall to the other, to create an opening at which a spreading fire may be cut off
17. Technique using smoke ejectors to develop artificial air flow and to pull smoke out of a structure
18. Movement of smoke being blown out of a ventilation opening only to be drawn back inside by the negative pressure created by the ejector because the open area around the ejector has not been sealed
19. A single cut the width of the saw blade made in a roof to check for fire extension

Down

2. Method of ventilating a room or structure by mechanically blowing fresh air through an inlet opening into the space in sufficient volume to create a slight positive pressure within and thereby forcing the contaminated atmosphere out the exit opening
3. Ventilating at a point above the fire through existing or created openings and channeling the contaminated atmosphere vertically within the structure and out the top
4. Any means other than natural ventilation. This type of ventilation may involve the use of blowers, and smoke ejectors
5. Ventilation accomplished by using a spray stream to draw the smoke from a compartment through an exterior opening
6. Fans that are used to push fresh air into a structure
8. Any technique by which heat, smoke, and other products of combustion are channeled horizontally out of a structure by way of existing or created horizontal openings such as windows, doors, or other openings in walls
10. The movement of air toward burning fuel and the movement of smoke out of the compartment or structure
11. Intended and controlled exhaust locations that are created or improved at or near the fire to allow products of combustion to escape the building
12. Phenomenon of a strong air draft moving from ground level to the roof level of a building
14. The side or direction from which the wind is blowing
15. Rectangular exhaust opening cut in a roof, allowing a section of roof deck (still nailed to a center rafter) to be tilted, thus creating an opening similar to a louver

1
2
3
4
5
6
7
8
9
10
11
12
13
14
15
16
17
18
19

Chapter 14

Water Supply

Terms

Write the definition of the terms below on the blanks provided.

1. **Gravity System (787)** ______________________________

____

2. **Direct Pumping System (787)** ______________________________

____

3. **Combination System (788)** ______________________________

____

4. **Water Main (789)** ______________________________

____

5. **Gate Valve (791)** ______________________________

____

6. **Butterfly Valve (791)** ______________________________

____

7. **Post Indicator Valve (PIV) (791)** ______________________________

____

8. **Outside Stem and Yoke (OS&Y) Valve (791)** ______________________________

____

9. **Flowmeter (792)** ______________________________

____

10. **Backflow Preventer (792)** ______________________________

11. **Dead-End Hydrant (793)** ______________________________

12. **Circulating Hydrant (793)** ______________________________

13. **Circulating Feed (793)** ______________________________

14. **Loop System (793)** ______________________________

15. **Dry-Barrel Hydrant (795)** ______________________________

16. **Wet-Barrel Hydrant (795)** ______________________________

17. **Pumper Outlet Nozzle (795)** ______________________________

18. **Steamer Connection (795)** ______________________________

19. **Drafting (799)** ______________________________

20. **Water Shuttle Operation (800)** ______________________________

21. **Portable Tank (801)** ______________________________

____

22. **Relay Pumping (803)** ______________________________

____

True/False

Write True or False on the blanks provided; if False, write the correct statement on the lines provided.

_______ 1. Lakes are natural freshwater sources that may be used by firefighters. (784)

____

____

_______ 2. Most direct pumping systems are found at mountain reservoirs. (788)

____

____

_______ 3. Primary feeders range from 16 inches (400 mm) to 72 inches (1 825 mm) in diameter. (789)

____

____

_______ 4. Access to the water supply system may be made through fire hydrants. (790)

____

____

_______ 5. Storage tanks range from 2,000 gallons (7 570 L) to over 10,000 gallons (37 850 L). (790)

____

____

_______ 6. Most private-system isolation valves are non-indicating. (791)

____

____

_______ 7. Friction loss may be caused by encrustations of minerals and sediment that accumulate over a period of years. (792-793)

_______ 8. Wet-barrel hydrants are usually installed in warmer climates. (795)

_______ 9. Fire hydrant markings can be used to designate water pressure. (795)

_______ 10. If a dry-barrel hydrant is not draining in winter, it must be pumped until empty. (798)

_______ 11. The most important consideration in alternative water supplies is contamination. (799)

_______ 12. Rural water supply operations are necessary in areas lacking public water distribution systems. (800)

_______ 13. The water supply volume of a water shuttle operation can be calculated based on the complete round trip. (802)

_______ 14. Relay pumping can be used in situations where the water source is very far away from the fire scene. (803)

Multiple Choice

Write the correct answers on the blanks provided.

_____ 1. Which type of water supply system may serve a particular area such as a residential subdivision? (784)

A. Public system
B. Private system
C. Natural system
D. Industrial system

_____ 2. Gravity systems are adequate only when the primary water source is located more than ___ feet (m) higher than the highest point in the water distribution system. (787)

A. 50 (15)
B. 100 (30)
C. 150 (45)
D. 200 (60)

_____ 3. Which of the following is an interlocking network of water mains that compose a water distribution system? (789)

A. Web
B. Grid
C. Pyramid
D. Network

_____ 4. Which of the following may form an intermediate grid between secondary feeders? (789)

A. Distributors
B. Control valves
C. Indicator valves
D. Primary feeders

_____ 5. The location of isolation valves is intended to disrupt the: (791)

A. minimum number of customers.
B. maximum number of customers.
C. minimum number of fire hydrants.
D. maximum number of fire hydrants.

_____ 6. Which of the following prohibits any water from flowing back into the public water system? (792)

A. Control valve
B. Isolation valve
C. Water flowmeter
D. Backflow preventer

_____ 7. Additional hydrants may be required where distances between intersections exceed: (792)

A. 150 to 250 feet (45 m to 75 m).
B. 250 to 350 feet (75 m to 105 m).
C. 350 to 400 feet (105 m to 120 m).
D. 400 to 550 feet (120 m to 165 m).

_____ 8. Regulations for the number of threads per inch on a fire hydrant is set by NFPA®: (795)

A. 472.
B. 1001.
C. 1492.
D. 1963.

_____ 9. On dry-barrel hydrants, the stem nut used to open and close the control valve is located on the: (795)

A. hose outlet.
B. pumper outlet.
C. top of the hydrant.
D. bottom of the hydrant.

_____ 10. What is the minimum size typically used to ensure adequate quantities of water through a water distribution system? (790)

A. 4-inch (100 mm).
B. 8-inch (200 mm).
C. 10-inch (250 mm).
D. 12-inch (300 mm).

_____ 11. Which of the following is a step in operating wet-barrel hydrants? (797)

A. Ensure that the valve is open.
B. Operate by using a ¼-turn valve.
C. Tighten the discharge caps that will be used.
D. Stand on the opposite side of the hydrant from the open discharge outlet.

_____ 12. Alternative water supplies should be ___ during preincident planning. (799)

A. tested

B. flushed

C. recorded

D. inspected

_____ 13. Which of the following statements regarding portable tanks is MOST accurate? (802)

A. They should be located near the fill site.

B. There should only be one tank set up at a time.

C. They should be located as close to the fire as possible.

D. They should be as level as possible to ensure maximum capacity.

_____ 14. To fill a mobile water supply apparatus quickly, use: (803)

A. the best fill site.

B. smaller hoselines.

C. the closest hydrant.

D. another mobile water supply apparatus.

_____ 15. In a relay pumping operation, the apparatus with the greatest pumping capacity should be located at the: (803)

A. fill site.

B. dump site.

C. fire scene.

D. water source.

Short Answer

Write the correct answers on the blanks provided.

1. What situations may limit the use of a water treatment facility for firefighting operations? (786)

____

____

____

____

2. Isolation and control valves are used to interrupt water flow to what parts of a water distribution and supply system? (791)

3. What factors other than distance affect the location and spacing of fire hydrants? (792)

4. List four things that can result in fire hydrant failure or a reduction in water supply. (793-794)

5. List five potential problems to be looking for when inspecting hydrants. (798-799)

6. What are the key components of a water shuttle? (801)

Crossword Puzzle

Across

2. Fire hydrant that receives water from two or more directions
5. Process of acquiring water from a static source and transferring it into a pump that is above the source's level; atmospheric pressure on the water surface forces the water into the pump where a partial vacuum was created
6. Fire hydrant outlet that is 4 inches (100 mm) in diameter or larger
8. A type of valve used to control underground water mains that provides a visual means for indicating "open" or "shut" position; found on the supply main of installed fire protection systems
9. Fire hydrant that has its operating valve located at the base or foot of the hydrant rather than in the barrel of the hydrant
15. A type of control valve for a sprinkler system in which the position of the center screw indicates whether the valve is open or closed
16. A check valve that prevents water from flowing back into a system and contaminating it
17. Use of two or more pumpers to move water over a long distance by operating them in series
18. Fire hydrant that is located on a secondary feeder or distributor main that receives water from two directions
19. Water supply system supplied directly by a system of pumps rather than elevated storage tanks

Down

1. Fire hydrant located on a dead-end main that receives water from only one direction
3. Water supply system that is a combination of both gravity and direct pumping systems
4. Method of water supply by which mobile water supply apparatus continuously transport water between a fill site and the dump site located near the emergency scene
7. Large-diameter outlet, usually 4½ inches (115 mm), at a hydrant or at the base of an elevated water storage container
8. Storage tank used during a relay or shuttle operation to hold water from water tanks or hydrants. This water can then be used to supply attack apparatus
10. Fire hydrant that has water all the way up to the discharge outlets; may have separate valves for each discharge or one valve for all the discharges
11. A principal pipe in a system of pipes for conveying water, especially one installed underground
12. Water main arranged in a complete circuit so that water will be supplied to a given point from more than one direction
13. Mechanical device installed in a discharge line that senses the amount of water flowing and provides a readout in units of gallons per minute (liters per minute)
14. Water supply system that relies entirely on the force of gravity to create pressure and cause water to flow through the system

1
2
3
4
5
6
7
8
9
10
11
12
13
14
15
16
17
18
19

Chapter 15

Fire Hose

Terms

Write the definition of the terms below on the blanks provided.

1. **Fire Hose (816)** ____________________

2. **Supply Hose (816)** ____________________

3. **Attack Hose (816)** ____________________

4. **Fire Department Connection (FDC) (816)** ____________________

5. **Soft Sleeve Hose (818)** ____________________

6. **Suction Hose (818)** ____________________

7. **Hard-Suction Hose (820)** ____________________

8. **Threaded Coupling (821)** ____________________

9. **Nonthreaded Coupling (821)** ____________________

10. **Shank (821)** ______________________________

11. **Higbee Cut (821)** ______________________________

12. **Higbee Indicators (821)** ______________________________

13. **Spanner Wrench (822)** ______________________________

14. **Quarter-Turn Coupling (823)** ______________________________

15. **Storz Coupling (823)** ______________________________

16. **Wye (835)** ______________________________

17. **Siamese (835)** ______________________________

18. **Water Thief (835)** ______________________________

19. **Adapter (835)** ______________________________

20. **Fitting (835)** ______________________________

21. **Reducer (838)** ______________________________

____

22. **Hydrant Wrench (842)** ______________________________

____

23. **Hose Bed (846)** ______________________________

____

24. **Finish (847)** ______________________________

____

25. **Flat Load (847)** ______________________________

____

26. **Accordion Load (848)** ______________________________

____

27. **Horseshoe Load (848)** ______________________________

____

28. **Dutchman (852)** ______________________________

____

29. **Preconnect (852)** ______________________________

____

30. **Booster Hoseline (855)** ______________________________

____

31. **Four-Way Hydrant Valve (856)** ______________________________

____

32. **Open Butt (871)** ______________________________

____

True/False

Write True or False on the blanks provided; if False, write the correct statement on the lines provided.

_______ 1. Attack hose transports water or other agents, at increased pressure, from a source (such as the building standpipe) to the point where water is applied to the fire. (816)

____

____

_______ 2. The traditional length of a section of fire hose in North America is 100 feet (30 m). (818)

____

____

_______ 3. On threaded couplings, the male part is cut on the exterior surface. (821)

____

____

_______ 4. Nonthreaded couplings are connected with locks or cams rather than screw threads. (823)

____

____

_______ 5. Hard-rubber booster hose must be washed with mild soap or detergent. (832)

____

____

_______ 6. Hard intake hose must be thoroughly dried before being reloaded. (832)

____

____

_______ 7. Fittings are used to connect hose of different diameters and thread types. (838)

____

____

_______ 8. A reverse horseshoe finish can be used on any size attack hose. (850)

_______ 9. Preconnected hose loads for attack lines are typically carried in the main hose bed. (852)

_______ 10. In a forward lay, hose is deployed from the water source to the incident. (856)

_______ 11. Making a hard intake connection is easier than connecting soft intake hose. (860)

_______ 12. When advancing a charged hoseline, the working line drag is the quickest and easiest way. (862)

_______ 13. When advancing hoseline up and down a stairway, hose should be charged when conditions allow. (863)

_______ 14. Improvising a standpipe may be necessary in buildings less than three stories. (865)

_______ 15. One firefighter may operate a large hoseline during exposure protection or overhaul operations. (869)

Identification

Identify the following items on the lines provided.

Hose Rolls (844-846)

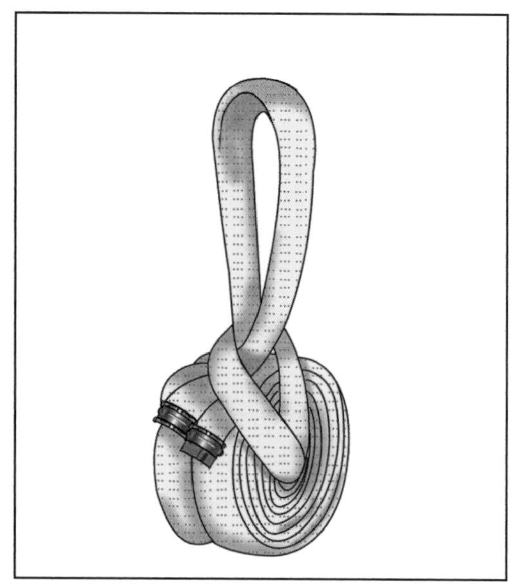

1. ______________________________

2. ______________________________

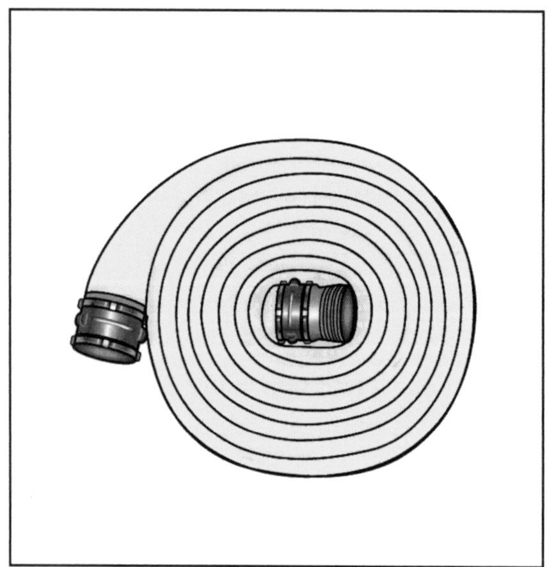

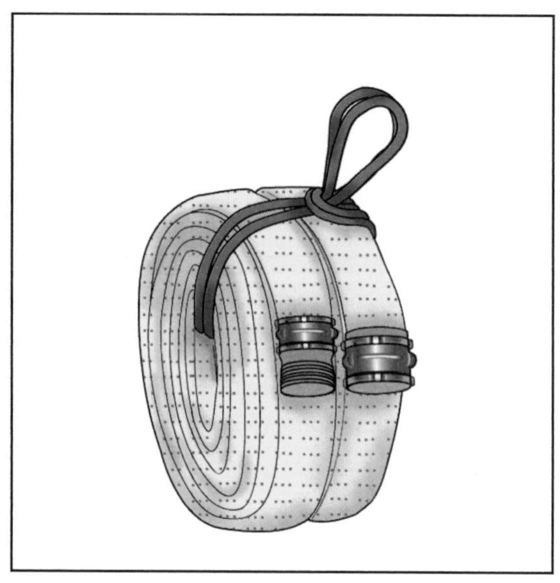

3. ______________________________

4. ______________________________

Hose Loads (846-851)

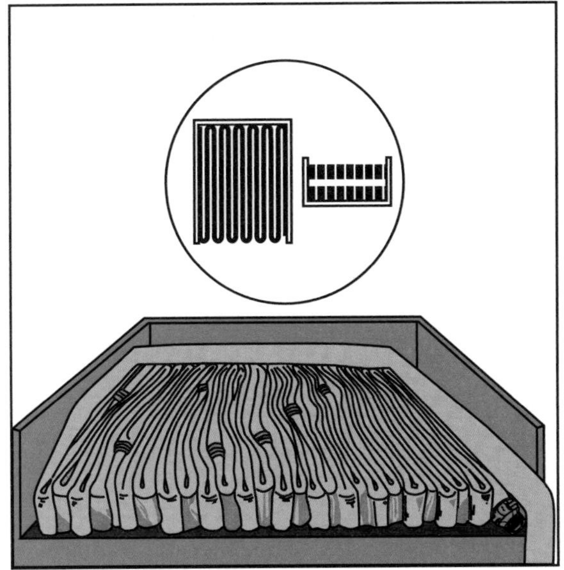

1. ______________________________

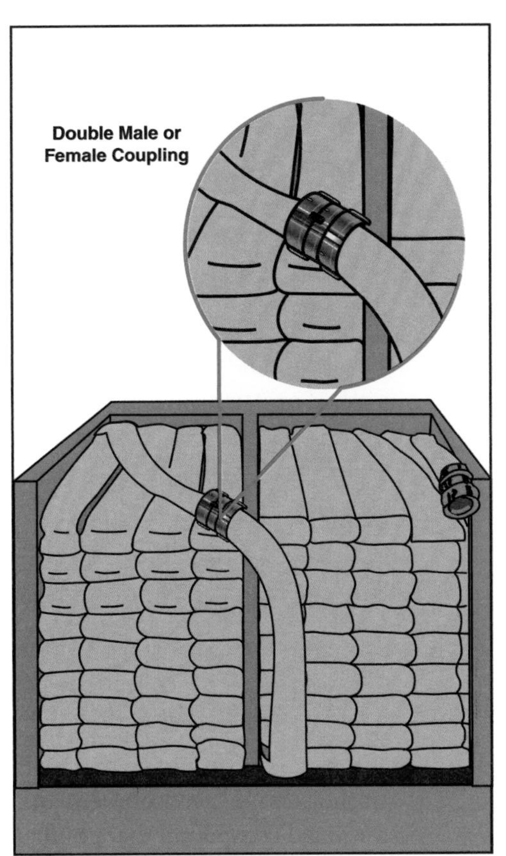

2. ______________________________

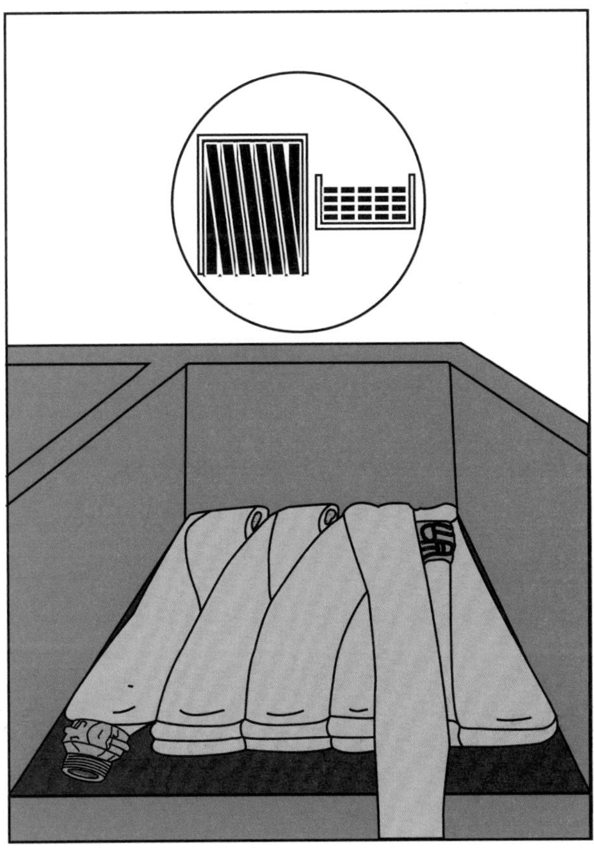

3. ______________________________

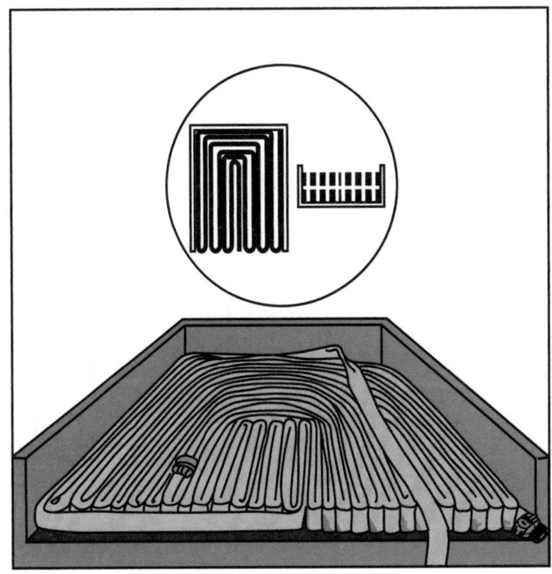

4. ______________________________

Matching

Write the correct answers on the blanks provided.

Causes of Fire Hose Damage

Match the description of fire hose damage with the type of damage. Each choice will be used only once.

_______ 1. Occurs when contact with an object or surface causes slices, rips, and abrasions on the exterior covering, crushed or damaged couplings, and cracked inner linings (825-826)

_______ 2. Can result from exposure to excess heat or cold temperatures (826-827)

_______ 3. Caused when hose with woven-jacket of cotton or other natural fiber is stored wet (827-828)

_______ 4. Caused by exposure to petroleum products, paints, acids, or alkalis weakening the hose to the point of bursting under pressure (828-829)

_______ 5. Chemical process in which metal is attacked by some substance in the environment and is converted to an unwanted compound that gradually weakens or destroys metal (829)

_______ 6. Can cause deterioration and cracking between folds; may occur if hose is left hanging in tower for excessive periods of time (830)

A. Age Deterioration
B. Chemical Damage
C. Corrosion
D. Mechanical Damage
E. Organic Damage
F. Thermal Damage

Types of Valves

Match the valve description with the type of fire hose valve. Each choice will be used only once.

_______ 1. Used in pumper discharged and gated wyes (836)

_______ 2. Used to control flow from hydrant (836)

_______ 3. Incorporate flat baffle that turns 90 degrees (836)

_______ 4. Used in Siamese appliances and FDC to allow water to flow in one direction only (836)

A. Ball Valves
B. Butterfly Valves
C. Clapper Valves
D. Gate Valves

Hose Tools

Match the description to the hose tool. Each choice will be used only once.

_________ 1. Protects hose from mechanical damage of dragging over sharp corners (840)

_________ 2. Can be installed when hoseline ruptures but must remain charged to continue the fire attack (840)

_________ 3. Can be used to stop the flow of water in a hoseline for various reasons (841)

_________ 4. Tightens or loosens couplings; has a number of other features built in (842)

_________ 5. Used to remove discharge caps from fire hydrant outlets and to open fire hydrant valves (842)

_________ 6. Sometimes used to strike lugs to tighten or loosen intake hose couplings (842)

_________ 7. Help prevent damage to fire hose when vehicles must drive over it (842)

_________ 8. Device used to protect fire hose from vibrating and rubbing against other surfaces (842)

_________ 9. Used to carry, pull, or handle charged hoselines (844)

A. Chafing block
B. Hose bridge or ramp
C. Hose clamp
D. Hose jacket
E. Hose roller
F. Hose strap, hose rope, and hose chain
G. Hydrant wrench
H. Rubber mallet
I. Spanner wrench

Multiple Choice

Write the correct answers on the blanks provided.

_____ 1. Which of the following is used to describe hose size? (818)

A. Width
B. Length
C. Diameter
D. Section size

_____ 2. Which type of fire hose has two female or nonthreaded couplings? (818-820)

A. Booster hose
B. Soft sleeve hose
C. Hard suction hose
D. Suction supply hose

_____ 3. Which types of fire hose couplings are very weak and only found on occupant-use fire hose? (821)

A. Cast
B. Brass
C. Extruded
D. Drop forged

_____ 4. What part of a threaded coupling is the portion that serves as the point of attachment to the hose? (821)

A. Shank
B. Male part
C. Higbee cut
D. Female part

_____ 5. What types of lugs are normally found on booster hose? (822)

A. Pin lugs
B. Rocker lugs
C. Handle lugs
D. Recessed lugs

_____ 6. Which of the following is an advantage of nonthreaded couplings? (824)

A. Fire hose can be quickly connected.
B. Fire hose cannot become uncoupled.
C. Hydrants do not require an adapter to make connections.
D. Dirt and debris cannot become lodged inside the coupling's grooves.

_____ 7. When should fire hose inspection be scheduled? (831)

A. Once per shift
B. After every third or fourth use
C. At least annually after first use
D. Within 120 days of being placed in service for the first time

_____ 8. Which of the following statements regarding a hose-washing machine is MOST accurate? (832)

A. It requires two or three people to operate.
B. The flow of water can be adjusted as desired.
C. It must be used outside the station or at the fire scene.
D. The most common type washes fire hose under 2 inches (50 mm).

_____ 9. How should hose be stored in racks in order to prevent damage? (834)

A. Store hose in direct sunlight
B. Locate racks in apparatus bay
C. Pack cotton fabric as tight as possible
D. Store hose in rack so that couplings are not in walkways

_____ 10. Which types of valve devices combine multiple lines into one line? (837)

A. Wye appliances
B. Siamese appliances
C. Water thief appliances
D. Large-diameter hose appliances

_____ 11. Which preconnected hose load for an attack line is designed to be pulled by one person and must be completely removed from the bed before deploying the nozzle end of the hose? (854)

A. Minuteman load
B. Triple layer load
C. Combination load
D. Preconnected flat load

_____ 12. When making the hydrant connection for a hose lay, communication between the ___ is essential. (857)

A. Firefighter at hydrant and dispatcher
B. Driver/operator and firefighter at hydrant
C. Driver/operator and firefighter at incident
D. Firefighter at hydrant and firefighter at incident

_____ 13. Which type of hose lay is used when the pumper must first go to the fire location before laying supply line? (858)

A. Reverse lay
B. Forward lay
C. Supply hose lay
D. Combination lay

_____ 14. Which type of hose lay refers to any of a number of ways to lay multiple supply hose with a single engine? (861)

A. Reverse lay
B. Forward lay
C. Supply hose lay
D. Combination lay

_____ 15. What kind of preconnected hoseline is intended to be deployed without dragging hose on the ground? (861)

A. Flat load
B. Minuteman load
C. Triple layer load
D. Combination load

_____ 16. It is acceptable to connect to a standpipe on the fire floor only if the: (864)

A. fire is in the incipient stage.
B. standpipe is already charged.
C. hose is carried over an aerial ladder.
D. standpipe is in an enclosed stairway.

_____ 17. Which method of improvising a standpipe can be used for lower floors of high-rise buildings? (866)

A. Inside stretch
B. Outside stretch
C. Interior stairway stretch
D. Exterior stairway stretch

_____ 18. Which of the following should be done before advancing hose up a ladder? (867)

A. Drain hose if hose has already been charged
B. Remove the firefighter that is heeling the ladder
C. Place two firefighters on each section of the ladder
D. Ensure that the firefighter is strapped onto the ladder

_____ 19. Which method for operating small hoselines is the minimum number required for handling any attack line during interior structural operations? (869)

A. One-firefighter method
B. Two-firefighter method
C. Three-firefighter method
D. Four-firefighter method

_____ 20. What is the safest method for controlling a loose hoseline? (871)

A. Put a kink in the hose
B. Form a loop in the hoseline
C. Close the valve at the pump
D. Apply a hose clamp at a stationary point in the hoseline

Short Answer

Write the correct answers on the lines provided.

1. In what four configurations is fire hose manufactured? (816)

2. How can frozen fire hose be removed from an ice-covered surface? (827)

3. What deficiencies should be corrected or reported when inspecting fire hose? (831)

4. What are the guidelines for caring for fire hose couplings? (834-835)

5. List three guidelines for loading hose. (852)

6. What are the guidelines for laying hose? (856)

7. List four safety guidelines for advancing hose into a structure. (862-863)

Crossword Puzzle

Across

4. Nonthreaded (sexless) coupling with two hook-like lugs that slip over a ring on the opposite coupling and then rotate 90 degrees clockwise to lock

5. Rigid, noncollapsible hose that operates under vacuum conditions without collapsing, allowing a pumping apparatus or portable pump to "draft" water from static or nonpressurized sources that are below the level of the fire pump

7. Noncollapsible rubber-covered, rubber-lined hose usually wound on a reel and mounted somewhere on the apparatus and used for extinguishment of incipient and smoldering fires

9. Large diameter, collapsible piece of hose used to connect a fire pump to a pressurized water supply source; sometimes incorrectly referred to as soft suction hose

12. Fitting used to attach a smaller hose to a larger hose

14. Extra fold placed along the length of a section of hose as it is loaded so that its coupling rests in proper position

15. Attack hose connected to a discharge when the hose is loaded; this shortens the time it takes to deploy the hose for fire fighting

16. Hose appliance with one female inlet and multiple male outlets, usually smaller than the inlet

Down

1. A flexible, portable tube manufactured from water tight materials in 50 to 100 foot (15 to 30 m) lengths that is used to transport water from a source or pump to the point it is discharged to extinguish fire

2. Device for connecting hose couplings with dissimilar threads but with the same inside diameter

3. Arrangement of hose usually placed on top of a hose load and connected to the end of the load

5. Special cut at the beginning of the thread on a hose coupling that provides positive identification of the first thread to eliminate cross threading

6. Coupling with no distinct male or female components

8. Hose that is used by trained firefighters to combat fires

10. Nonthreaded (sexless) coupling commonly found on large-diameter hose

11. Hose that is designed for the purpose of moving water between a water source and a pump that is supplying attack hoselines or fire suppression systems

13. Device that facilitates the connection of hoselines to provide an uninterrupted flow of extinguishing agent

1
2
3
4
5
6
7
8
9
10
11
12
13
14
15
16

15

Terms

Write the definition of the terms below on the blanks provided.

1. **Service Test (872)** ______________________________

____

True/False

Write True or False on the blanks provided; if False, write the correct statement on the lines provided.

_______ 1. Fire hose should be tested annually, after repairs have been made, and after a vehicle has run over the hose. (872)

____

____

_______ 2. If defects are found during service testing, hose should be removed from service immediately. (872)

____

____

_______ 3. When service testing hose, connect the hose to discharges on the pump panel side of the apparatus. (873)

____

____

Multiple Choice

Write the correct answers on the blanks provided.

_____ 1. The area for service testing fire hose should be: (872)

A. relatively dark.
B. completely flat.
C. very close to the station.
D. large enough to lay hose in straight lines.

Firefighter II

_____ 2. Which of the following is a guideline for service testing fire hose? (873)

A. Close all valves quickly
B. Keep hose testing area dry
C. Test lengths 50 feet (15 m) or shorter
D. Exercise extra care when the fire hose is uncharged

Short Answer

Write the correct answers on the lines provided.

1. What equipment should be used for service testing? (872)

____

____

____

____

____

____

Chapter 16

Fire Streams

Firefighter I

Terms

Write the definition of the terms below on the blanks provided.

1. Specific Heat (944) ____

2. Latent Heat of Vaporization (944) ____

3. Friction Loss (947) ____

4. Water Hammer (949) ____

5. Fire Stream (949) ____

6. Critical Flow Rate (951) ____

7. Solid Stream (951) ____

8. Smooth Bore Nozzle (951) ____

9. Nozzle Pressure (954) ____

10. **Fog Stream (954)** ___

11. **Fog Nozzle (954)** ___

12. **Straight Stream (955)** ___

13. **Broken Stream (955)** ___

14. **Master Stream (957)** ___

15. **Ball Valve (963)** ___

16. **Nozzle Reaction (964)** ___

True/False

Write True or False on the blanks provided; if False, write the correct statement on the lines provided.

___ 1. The primary way water extinguishes fire is by absorbing heat. (944)

___ 2. Water broken into small particles absorbs heat less rapidly than water in a compact solid stream. (946)

_______ 3. Steam produced during fire fighting is an unintended byproduct of water used as an extinguishing agent. (946)

_______ 4. To extinguish a fire by cooling, the heat absorbing capability of the fire stream must exceed the heat output of the fire. (951)

_______ 5. Once the nozzle pressure has produced a fog stream with maximum reach, increasing nozzle pressure does little more than increase the volume of water flowing. (955)

_______ 6. NFPA® 1963 establishes three general categories of nozzles; straight tip, spray, and piercing. (957)

_______ 7. A cellar nozzle is usually controlled by a valve located one section of hose away from the nozzle. (962)

_______ 8. Rotary control valves control both the flow of water and the discharge pattern of the fire stream. (963)

_______ 9. As a fog pattern widens, the nozzle reaction increases and the nozzle becomes more difficult to handle. (966)

_______ 10. Basic nozzle maintenance, care, and cleaning should always be performed according to the manufacturer's recommendations. (966)

Fill in the Blank

Write the correct answer on the blanks provided.

1. During a training evolution, the operator of a handline quickly closed the nozzle control valve. The hoseline and water pump were damaged by the resulting pressure surge, referred to as ________________. (949)

2. Observations and tests classify streams that do not lose continuity until after the breakover point and that are cohesive enough to maintain their original shape and attain the required height as ______________. (954)

3. Large volume fire streams are created by apparatus-mounted pipes. These streams, which can be fed by one or more 2½- or 3-inch (65 mm or 77 mm) hoselines or large-diameter hoselines, are called ________________. (951)

4. One type of valve, when fully open, gives maximum flow and performance. This valve, which provides effective control with minimum effort, is the ______________________. (963)

5. Water flowing from a nozzle creates a force in the direction of the stream and equal force in the opposite direction, pushing back against the operator. This force that acts against the nozzle and the curves in the hoseline, and can make the nozzle difficult to handle, is called ____________________. (964)

Matching

Write the correct answers on the blanks provided.

Fire Stream Pattern Size

Match the fire stream size with the fire stream characteristic. Each choice may be used more than once.

________	1. Discharges less than 40 gpm (160 L/min) (950)	A. Master stream
________	2. Discharges more than 350 gpm (1 400 L/min) (951)	B. Handline stream
________	3. Discharges from 40 to 350 gpm (160 L/min to 1 400 L/min) (950)	C. Low-volume stream
________	4. Is supplied by large-diameter hoselines (951)	
________	5. Is supplied by 1½- to 3-inch (38 mm to 77 mm) hose (950)	
________	6. Is supplied by one or more 2½- or 3-inch (65 mm or 77 mm) hoselines (951)	
________	7. Is supplied by ¾-inch (20 mm), 1-inch (25 mm), or 1½-inch (38 mm) hoselines (950)	

Fire Stream Pattern Types

Match the fire stream pattern type with the pattern characteristic. Each choice may be used more than once.

_____ 1. Compact stream with little shower or spray (951)

_____ 2. Fine spray composed of tiny water droplets (954-955)

_____ 3. Stream broken into coarsely divided droplets (955-956)

_____ 4. Produced by fixed orifice, smooth bore nozzle (951)

_____ 5. Has characteristics most similar to solid stream (955)

_____ 6. Able to reach areas other streams might not reach (951)

_____ 7. Created by cellar, penetrating, and chimney nozzles (955-956)

_____ 8. Semi-solid stream produced by an adjustable nozzle (955)

_____ 9. Can be used for crew protection, and to cool the hot fire gas layer (954-955)

_____ 10. Exposes maximum surface for greatest heat absorption per gallon (liter) (954-955)

_____ 11. Produces less steam conversion and less heat absorption per gallon (liter) (951)

_____ 12. Can have narrow to wide pattern produced by adjustable pattern nozzle (954-955)

_____ 13. Used to extinguish fires in attics, cocklofts, basements and other enclosed spaces (955-956)

A. Fog-stream

B. Solid stream

C. Broken-stream

D. Straight stream

Fog Nozzles

Match the fog nozzle type with the nozzle description. Each choice will be used only once.

_____ 1. An adjustable-pattern fog nozzle in which the rated discharge is delivered at a designated nozzle pressure and nozzle setting (959)

_____ 2. An adjustable-pattern fog nozzle in which the pressure remains relatively constant through a range of discharge rates (961)

_____ 3. An adjustable pattern fog nozzle that discharges a constant discharge rate throughout the range of patterns at a designed nozzle pressure (959)

_____ 4. A constant discharge rate fog nozzle with a feature that allows manual adjustment of the orifice to affect a predetermined discharge rate while the nozzle is flowing (961)

A. Basic fog nozzle

B. Constant gallonage fog nozzle

C. Constant/select gallonage fog nozzle

D. Constant pressure (automatic) fog nozzle

Multiple Choice

Write the correct answers on the blanks provided.

_____ 1. Which of the following statements about vaporization is MOST accurate? (944)

A. Energy is required to raise the temperature of water to the boiling point, but not to convert the water to steam.

B. Approximately 970 Btu/lb (2257 kJ/kg) is required to vaporize water at the boiling point.

C. Approximately 970 Btu/lb (2257 kJ/kg) is required to raise the temperature of water one degree.

D. At the boiling point, water vaporized into steam expands approximately 100 times its original volume.

_____ 2. Which of the following will cause the upper layer of hot smoke and fire gases in a compartment to expand downward? (946-947)

A. Steam formed in contact with hot surfaces

B. Steam formed in the upper layer of hot fire gases

C. Steam formed at temperatures below 212°F (100°C)

D. Steam formed in the layers of hot fire gases closest to the floor

_____ 3. Which of the following statements about friction loss is MOST accurate? (947-948)

A. Friction decreases pressure at the nozzle.

B. Friction has little effect on the rate of water flow.

C. The longer the hose lay, the lower the friction loss.

D. The fewer adapters in the hose lay, the higher the friction loss.

_____ 4. An increase in water pressure at the nozzle might be caused by: (948)

A. adding bends to the hose lay.

B. increasing the number of adapters.

C. increasing the length of the hose lay.

D. placing the nozzle below the fire pump.

_____ 5. Which of the following statements about water pressure is MOST accurate? (948)

A. Gravity has little effect on nozzle pressure.

B. If the nozzle is above the fire pump, nozzle pressure is decreased.

C. If the nozzle is below the fire pump, nozzle pressure is decreased.

D. Adjusting pump pressure has little effect in overcoming elevation loss/gain.

_____ 6. Which of the following statements about water hammer is MOST accurate? (949)
   A. Water hammer is caused by closing nozzles too slowly.
   B. Water hammer is caused by air and turbulence in hoselines.
   C. Water hammer creates a startling noise, but no real damage.
   D. The effects of water hammer increase significantly at higher flow rates.

_____ 7. Fire stream patterns are defined by the volume of water flowing from the nozzle per minute and the: (950)
   A. nozzle reaction force.
   B. water source that is used for the specific fire stream.
   C. the specific type of fuel that the fire stream is being used on.
   D. specific pattern or shape of the water after it leaves the nozzle.

_____ 8. Which of the following statements about fire stream types is NOT correct? (951)
   A. Each fire stream pattern type is matched to one specific size classification.
   B. An effective fire stream must have sufficient reach to put water where it is needed.
   C. To extinguish a fire by cooling, a fire stream must meet or exceed the critical flow rate.
   D. A fire stream pattern must be compact enough for the majority of the water to reach the burning material.

_____ 9. Which of the following are required for effective fire streams? (951)
   A. Pump and hoseline
   B. Fuel and foam creation
   C. Hoseline and slight wind
   D. Fuel and back-up water sources

_____ 10. Which of the following is NOT a characteristic of an effective fire stream? (951)
   A. Pattern must meet or exceed critical flow rate
   B. Must have sufficient reach to put water where needed
   C. Pattern type must match appropriate size classification
   D. Pattern must be compact enough for water to reach burning material

_____ 11. In actual operation, fire stream angles between ___ provide maximum reach. (956)
   A. 20 to 24 degrees
   B. 30 to 34 degrees
   C. 40 to 45 degrees
   D. 45 to 49 degrees

_____ 12. Which of the following statements about smooth bore nozzles is MOST accurate? (959)

A. Smooth bore nozzles operate at high nozzle pressures.
B. Smooth bore nozzles are more prone to clogging with debris.
C. Smooth bore nozzles may be adjusted, resulting in different patterns.
D. Smooth bore nozzles on handlines are usually operated at 50 psi (305 kPa).

_____ 13. Which of the following nozzles creates a straight stream? (959)

A. Fog nozzle
B. Cellar nozzle
C. Smooth bore nozzle
D. Master stream delivery device

_____ 14. Which of the following nozzles is used to apply water in confined spaces that attack hoselines cannot reach? (962)

A. Piercing nozzle
B. Stacked tip nozzle
C. Smooth bore nozzle
D. Adjustable fog nozzle

_____ 15. Which of the following nozzle control valves stops the flow of water by rotating a smooth waterway perpendicular to the flow of water? (963)

A. Ball valve
B. Slide valve
C. Standpipe valve
D. Rotary control valve

_____ 16. Which of the following statements about maintaining nozzles is MOST accurate? (966)

A. Nozzles should be inspected after each use, and at least weekly.
B. Nozzles should be stored with the control bale in the open position.
C. Technical maintenance should be performed by qualified technicians.
D. Nozzles should be thoroughly cleaned after each use with powdered kitchen cleanser and steel wool.

Short Answer

Write the correct answers on the lines provided.

1. What are four characteristics of water that make it valuable for fire extinguishment? (944)

2. How does friction affect water flow and nozzle pressure? (947)

3. What are the factors that affect fire streams? (949)

4. What are four uses of fire streams? (949-950)

5. What two factors determine the volume of water discharged by a fire stream? (951)

6. What are the three main functions of nozzles and broken-stream delivery devices? (957)

____

____

____

7. What are the three main steps in controlling a handline nozzle to overcome nozzle reaction? (964)

____

____

____

8. What are three actions that should be performed when inspecting nozzles? (966)

____

____

____

Crossword Puzzle

Across

3. Stream of water that has been broken into coarsely divided drops
5. Counterforce directed against a person holding a nozzle or a device holding a nozzle by the velocity of water being discharged
6. Velocity pressure at which water is discharged from the nozzle
7. Loss of pressure created by the turbulence of water moving against the interior walls of fire hose, pipes, fittings, and adapters
10. Stream of water or other water-based extinguishing agent after it leaves the fire hose and nozzle until it reaches the desired point
11. Fire stream of finely divided particles used for fire control
12. An adjustable pattern nozzle equipped with a shut off control device
14. The minimum flow rate at which extinguishment can be achieved
15. Amount of energy required to raise the temperature of a specified unit mass of a material 1 degree in temperature
16. Valve having a ball-shaped internal component with a hole through its center that permits water to flow through when aligned with the waterway

Down

1. Force created by the rapid deceleration of water causing a violent increase in pressure that can be powerful enough to rupture piping or damage fixtures, generally results from closing a valve or nozzle too quickly
2. Quantity of heat absorbed by a substance at the point at which it changes from a liquid to a vapor
4. Large-caliber water stream usually supplied by combining two or more hoselines into a manifold device or by fixed piping that delivers 350 gpm (1 325 L/min) or more
8. Semi-solid stream that is produced by a fog nozzle
9. A nozzle with a straight, smooth tip, designed to produce a solid fire stream
13. Hose stream that stays together as a solid mass, as opposed to a fog or spray stream; a solid stream is produced by a smooth bore nozzle and should not be confused with a straight stream

1
2
3
4
5
6
7
8
9
10
11
12
13
14
15
16

16

Terms

Write the definition of the terms below on the blanks provided.

1. **Foam (967)** ______________________________

2. **Foam Concentrate (968)** ______________________________

3. **Foam Proportioner (968)** ______________________________

4. **Foam Solution (968)** ______________________________

5. **Finished Foam (968)** ______________________________

6. **Foam Expansion (969)** ______________________________

7. **Class A Foam (971)** ______________________________

8. **Surfactant (971)** ______________________________

9. **Surface Tension (971)** ______________________________

10. **Class B Foam (972)** ______________________________

11. **Aqueous Film Forming Foam (AFFF) (972)** ______________________________

____

12. **Film Forming Fluoroprotein Foam (FFFP) (972)** ______________________________

____

13. **Viscous (973)** ______________________________

____

14. **pH (973)** ______________________________

____

15. **Proportioning (974)** ______________________________

____

16. **Eduction (975)** ______________________________

____

17. **Venturi Principle (975)** ______________________________

____

18. **Injection (975)** ______________________________

____

19. **Premixing (977)** ______________________________

____

20. **Compressed Air Foam System (CAFS) (978)** ______________________________

____

21. **In-Line Eductor (979)** ______________________________

____

22. **Handline Nozzle (981)** ______________________________

____

23. **Safety Data Sheet (SDS) (985)** ______________________________

____

True/False

Write True or False on the blanks provided; if False, write the correct statement on the lines provided.

_______ 1. Foam works by forming a blanket of foam on the surface of burning liquid and solid fuels. (967)

____

____

_______ 2. Foam concentrate, water, and air can be mixed in almost any proportion to produce good-quality foam. (968)

____

____

_______ 3. Fluorosurfactants are flammable liquids that mix readily with water. (968)

____

____

_______ 4. Ethanol or ethanol-based fuels require alcohol-resistant foams for extinguishment. (972)

____

____

_______ 5. In-line foam eductors are the most common type of foam proportioner currently in use. (979)

____

____

_______ 6. Compressed air foam systems are common portable foam proportioning devices. (980-981)

____

____

_________ 7. Smooth bore nozzles may be used to apply a wide range of foam solutions. (981)

____

____

_________ 8. Air-aspirating foam nozzles are the most effective appliance for the generation of low-expansion foam. (982)

____

____

_________ 9. When applying foam to a pool of liquid fuel, the operator should stop periodically to see if the fire is extinguished before the pool is covered. (984)

____

____

_________ 10. Foam concentrates can pose serious health risks to firefighters. (985)

____

____

Fill in the Blank

Write the correct answer on the blanks provided.

1. Class A foams will not extinguish Class B fires; Class B foams designed solely for hydrocarbon fires will not extinguish polar solvent fires. To be effective, foam concentrates must match _______________. (969)

2. For maximum effectiveness, foam concentrates must be proportioned at the specific percentage for which they were designed. Failure to follow proportioning procedures will result in __________________. (974)

3. In addition to a pump to supply water and a fire hose to transport it, two other pieces of equipment are needed to produce a foam fire stream: a foam proportioner and ______________________________. (978)

4. The ______________________________ adds air into the foam solution to produce finished foam. (978)

5. An appropriate amount of foam concentrate is introduced into the water stream by the ____________________. (978)

6. The two basic types of medium and high-expansion foam generating devices are water-aspirating type nozzles and ________________________. (983)

Matching

Write the correct answers on the blanks provided.

Ways Foam Extinguishes/Prevents Fire

Match the action of fire fighting foam with the description of that action. Each choice will be used only once.

_____ 1. Creates a barrier between the fuel and fire (967)

_____ 2. Lowers the temperature of the fuel and adjacent surfaces (967)

_____ 3. Prevents air from reaching the fuel and mixing with vapors and prevents the release of flammable vapors (967)

_____ 4. Lowers the surface tension of water and allows it to penetrate fires in Class A materials (967)

A. Cooling
B. Separating
C. Penetrating
D. Smothering

Foam Expansion

Match the foam expansion classification with the appropriate description. Each choice may be used more than once.

_____ 1. 20-to-1 air/solution ratio (967)

_____ 2. 20-to-1 to 200-to-1 air/solution ratios (967)

_____ 3. 200-to-1 to 1,000-to-1 air/solution ratios (967)

_____ 4. Used to suppress vapors from hazardous materials spills (967)

_____ 5. Synthetic foaming agents typically used in confined spaces (967)

_____ 6. Used through hydraulically-operated nozzle-style delivery devices (967)

_____ 7. Effective for controlling and extinguishing most Class B fires, and cooling and penetrating Class A fires (967)

A. Low-expansion foam
B. Medium-expansion foam
C. High-expansion foam

Foam Proportioning Methods

Match the foam proportioning method with the appropriate description. Each choice may be used more than once.

_______ 1. Simplest method of mixing foam concentrate and water (975-977)

_______ 2. Premeasured portions of water and foam concentrate are mixed in a container (977-978)

_______ 3. Commonly used to mix foam within fire apparatus water tank or portable tank (975-977)

_______ 4. Uses external pump or head pressure to force foam concentrate into fire stream (975)

_______ 5. Uses pressure energy in stream of water to induct foam concentrate into fire stream (975)

_______ 6. Pump may require additional maintenance due to degreasing properties of foam (975-977)

_______ 7. Commonly employed in apparatus-mounted or fixed fire protection system applications (975)

_______ 8. Depends on Venturi Principle to draw foam from concentrate container into water stream (975)

_______ 9. In most cases, solutions are discharged from a pressure-rated tank using compressed inert gas or air (977-978)

_______ 10. Typically used with portable extinguishers, wheeled extinguishers, and vehicle-mounted tank systems (977-978)

A. Injection

B. Eduction

C. Premixing

D. Batch-mixing

Foam Proportioning Systems

Match the foam proportioning system with the appropriate description. Each choice may be used more than once.

_______ 1. Hoseline contains finished foam (980-981)

_______ 2. Simplest and most common devices in use today (979)

_______ 3. Include in-line eductors and foam nozzle eductors (979)

_______ 4. Onboard air compressor adds air to create finished foam (980-981)

_______ 5. Include around-the-pump proportioners, and balanced pressure proportioners (980)

_______ 6. Commonly found on aircraft rescue and fire fighting apparatus (ARFF) and fire boats (980)

A. Portable foam proportioners

B. Apparatus-mounted proportioners

C. Compressed air foam systems (CAFS)

Firefighter II

16

Multiple Choice

Write the correct answers on the blanks provided.

_____ 1. Which action of fire fighting foam prevents air from reaching fuel and mixing with vapors and the release of flammable vapors, reducing the possibility of ignition or reignition? (967)

A. Cooling

B. Aerating

C. Penetrating

D. Smothering

_____ 2. Which of the following statements about fire fighting foams is MOST accurate? (967)

A. Class B foam is especially effective on wildland and brush fires.

B. Foam blankets are ineffective at suppressing vapors from unignited fuels.

C. Class A foam is especially effective on hydrocarbon fuels and polar solvents.

D. After controlling flames, Class A foam breaks down, releasing water and cooling solid fuel.

_____ 3. Fluoroprotein foams and ___ are effective at extinguishing fires and suppressing vapors on hydrocarbon fuels because they float on the surface of the fuel. (972)

A. protein foams

B. synthetic foams

C. specialized foams

D. alcohol-resistant foams

_____ 4. Which of the following statements about foam concentrates is MOST accurate? (973)

A. A foam blanket is of little benefit on unignited fuels.

B. Foam application rates are virtually the same for all polar solvents.

C. Foam application should be uninterrupted until extinguishment is complete.

D. The minimum rate of application will be marked on the foam concentrate container.

_____ 5. When selecting ratios for proportioning foam, operators should: (974)

A. consider the proportioner to be used.

B. follow the manufacturer's recommendations.

C. consult NFPA® 1963 for foam mixing guidelines.

D. start with a low proportion of foam and increase the ratio as needed.

_____ 6. Most foam concentrates are intended to be mixed with ___ percent water. (974)

A. 0.01 to 10

B. 0.1 to 6.0

C. 10 to 25.5

D. 94 to 99.9

_____ 7. Which of the following statements about compressed air foam systems (CAFS) is MOST accurate? (980)

A. Stream reach is typically shorter than with other foam systems.

B. There may be a high nozzle reaction when the nozzle is opened.

C. Hoselines filled with CAFS are heavier than those filled with water only.

D. An onboard air compressor adds air to the concentrate before mixing with water.

_____ 8. Which of the following statements about foam delivery devices is MOST accurate? (981)

A. Smooth bore nozzles are used only with Class B foams.

B. Solid agent foam concentrates may be used on Class A fires only.

C. Air-aspirating foam nozzles typically have a longer reach than standard fog nozzles.

D. Fog nozzles use the agitation of water droplets moving through air to generate foam.

_____ 9. Which of the following foam generators is typically associated with total-flooding applications? (983)

A. Fog nozzle

B. Air-aspirating type nozzle

C. Water-aspirating type nozzle

D. Mechanical blower generator

_____ 10. Poor-quality foam may result from: (983)

A. a short hose lay on the discharge side.

B. the nozzle being located too far below the eductor.

C. the nozzle not being fully open, restricting water flow.

D. using an eductor and nozzle with identical flow ratings.

_____ 11. Which application method is used for fuel spills on open ground? (984)

A. Roll-on method

B. Rain-down method

C. Total-flood method

D. Bank-down method

_____ 12. In which application method does the operator direct the foam stream into the air above the fire and allow the foam to float gently down onto the surface of the fuel? (985)

A. Roll-on method

B. Rain-down method

C. Total-flood method

D. Bank-down method

_____ 13. Which application method is used for fires contained in diked pools around storage tanks? (985)

A. Roll-on method
B. Rain-down method
C. Total-flood method
D. Bank-down method

_____ 14. Which of the following statements about finished foam in the environment is MOST accurate? (986)

A. Generally, protein-based foams are safer for the environment than other types of foam.
B. Manufacturers' safety data sheets (SDS) do not contain environmental impact information.
C. In a body of water, decomposing foam increases oxygen available to fish and other aquatic creatures.
D. In the United States, Class A foams should be approved by the U.S. Fish and Wildlife Service for environmental safety.

Short Answer

Write the correct answers on the lines provided.

1. List four examples of hydrocarbon fuels? (973)

____

____

____

____

2. List four examples of polar solvents? (972)

____

____

____

____

3. What are five types of foams available for specific applications and specialized uses? (973)

____

____

____

____

____

4. What are three factors to consider when selecting a foam proportioner? (974)

____

____

____

Crossword Puzzle

Across

1. Chemical compound solution that is mixed with water and air to produce finished foam
3. Chemical that lowers the surface tension of a liquid
6. Synthetic foam concentrate that, when combined with water, can form a complete vapor barrier over fuel spills and fires and is a highly effective extinguishing and blanketing agent on hydrocarbon fuels
11. Mixture of foam concentrate and water before the introduction of air
13. Method of proportioning foam that uses an external pump or head pressure to force foam concentrate into the fire stream at the correct ratio for the flow desired
14. Generic term used to describe a high-energy foam-generation system consisting of a water pump, a foam proportioning system, and an air compressor (or other air source) that injects air into the foam solution before it enters a hoseline
15. Physical law stating that when a fluid, such as water or air, is forced under pressure through a restricted orifice, there is an increase in the velocity of the fluid passing through the orifice and a corresponding decrease in the pressure exerted against the sides of the constriction
16. Process used to mix foam concentrate with water in a nozzle or proportioner; concentrate is drawn into the water stream by the Venturi method

Down

1. Completed product after air is introduced into the foam solution
2. Hydrocarbon-based surfactants that are essentially wetting agents that reduce the surface tension of water and allow it to soak into combustible materials easier than plain water
4. Foam concentrate that combines the qualities of fluoroprotein foam with those of aqueous film forming foam
5. Any nozzle that can be safely handled by one to three firefighters and flows less than 350 gpm (1 400 L/min)
7. Device that introduces foam concentrate into the water stream to make the foam solution
8. Foam fire-suppression agent designed for use on unignited or ignited Class B flammable or combustible liquids
9. Form provided by the manufacturer and blender of chemicals that contains information about chemical composition, physical and chemical properties, health and safety hazards, emergency response procedures, and waste disposal procedures of the specified material
10. Result of adding air to a foam solution consisting of water and foam concentrate
12. Mixing premeasured portions of water and foam concentrate in a container

1
2
3
4
5
6
7
8
9
10
11
12
13
14
15
16

Chapter 17

Fire Control

Firefighter I

Terms

Write the definition of the terms below on the blanks provided.

1. **Small-Diameter Hose (SDH) (1009)** ______________________________

____

2. **Direct Attack (Structural) (1013)** ______________________________

____

3. **Indirect Attack (Structural) (1014)** ______________________________

____

4. **Combination Attack (1014)** ______________________________

____

5. **Shielded Fire (1015)** ______________________________

____

6. **Exposures (1020)** ______________________________

____

7. **Exposure Protection (1020)** ______________________________

____

8. **High-Voltage (1023)** ______________________________

____

9. **Low-Voltage (1023)** ______________________________

____

10. **Liquefied Petroleum Gas (LPG) (1026)** ______________________________

____

11. **Polychlorinated Biphenyl (PCB) (1033)** ______________________________

____

12. **Topography (1052)** ______________________________

____

13. **Fusee (1054)** ______________________________

____

14. **Direct Attack (Ground Cover) (1054)** ______________________________

____

15. **Indirect Attack (Ground Cover) (1054)** ______________________________

____

True/False

Write True or False on the blanks provided; if False, write the correct statement on the lines provided.

_______ 1. An offensive attack is selected when there is no threat to occupant life. (1006)

____

____

_______ 2. Hoseline selection is critical for efficiency and safety. (1009)

____

____

_______ 3. When opening the door to an interior fire, wait 5-10 seconds to observe any reactions before entering the structure. (1013)

____

____

_______ 4. An indirect attack is a way of reducing heat release from the hot gas layer. (1015)

____

____

_______ 5. Large numbers of personnel may be required at fires in upper levels of structures to conduct evacuations. (1016)

____

____

_______ 6. In basement fires, an interior enclosed stairwell is the safest access point. (1019)

____

____

_______ 7. A risk/benefit analysis of a commercial basement fire is performed the same way as a residential basement fire. (1020)

____

____

_______ 8. In a residential structure, individual circuit breakers should be used to cut all power off. (1023)

____

____

_______ 9. Liquefied petroleum gas is explosive in concentrations between 5 and 15 percent. (1026)

____

____

_______ 10. Restoration of water utilities is the responsibility of the fire department. (1026)

____

____

_______ 11. A master stream device should be supplied with at least two 2½-inch (65 mm) hoselines. (1029)

____

____

_______ 12. For maximum safety, only utility personnel should cut electrical power lines. (1032)

_______ 13. Water is extremely effective on Class D fires. (1037)

_______ 14. Vehicle fires require full PPE including SCBA. (1038)

_______ 15. In engine compartment fires, the fire must be controlled before the hood can be opened. (1041)

_______ 16. Trash container fires require only standard firefighting gear. (1048)

_______ 17. Standard structural turnout clothing may be used in fighting ground cover fires. (1054)

Matching

Write the correct answers on the blanks provided.

Types of Control Valves

Match the descriptions with the type of control valve. Each choice will be used only once.

_______ 1. Has yoke on outside with threaded stem that opens and closes gate inside valve housing (1028)

_______ 2. Hollow metal post that houses valve stem (1028)

_______ 3. Extends horizontally through wall with target and valve operating nut on outside of building (1028)

_______ 4. Uses circular disk inside flat plate on top of valve housing (1028)

A. Outside stem and yoke

B. Post indicator valve

C. Post indicator valve assembly

D. Wall post indicator valve

Properties of Alternative Fuels

Match the properties with the alternative fuel. Each choice will be used only once.

_________ 1. Nontoxic; noncorrosive; has a narrow explosive range (1043-1044)

_________ 2. Clean burning; safer than gasoline; stored under pressure (1044)

_________ 3. Battery sole source of power; may not emit noise when engine is running (1045)

_________ 4. Water-soluble; electrically-conductive; has slight gasoline odor (1046)

_________ 5. Nontoxic; biodegradable; sulfur free (1046)

_________ 6. Colorless; odorless; nontoxic; energy efficient (1046)

A. Biodiesel
B. Electric
C. Ethanol/methanol
D. Hydrogen
E. Liquefied petroleum gas
F. Natural gas

Parts of a Ground Cover Fire

Match the descriptions with parts of a ground cover fire. Each choice will be used only once.

_________ 1. Area from where fire started (1052)

_________ 2. Part of ground cover that spreads most rapidly (1052)

_________ 3. Long narrow strip of fire extending from the main fire (1052)

_________ 4. Outer boundary, or distance around outside edge, of burning or burned area (1053)

_________ 5. Side opposite head (1053)

_________ 6. Sides, roughly parallel to main direction of fire spread (1053)

_________ 7. Caused by flying sparks or embers landing outside main fire (1053)

_________ 8. Patches of unburned fuel inside fire perimeter (1053)

_________ 9. Area of unburned fuels next to involved area (1053)

_________ 10. Opposite of green (1053)

A. Black
B. Finger
C. Flanks
D. Green
E. Head
F. Heel
G. Islands
H. Origin 1052
I. Perimeter
J. Spot Fire

Multiple Choice

Write the correct answers on the blanks provided.

_____ 1. Which strategic transition is necessary when the situation rapidly changes? (1007)

A. Indirect to direct
B. Direct to indirect
C. Offensive to defensive
D. Defensive to offensive

_____ 2. Which of the following determines the nozzle type selected? (1011)

A. Water pressure

B. Hose load type

C. Type of exposures

D. Available manpower

_____ 3. Which of the following is a pre-entry consideration critical to firefighter safety and effectiveness? (1012)

A. Ensuring that all tools are nonsparking

B. Determining number of personnel needed

C. Identifying potential emergency escape routes

D. Ensuring that personnel accountability devices are available if necessary

_____ 4. Which of the following steps should be taken when making an interior attack on a structure fire? (1012)

A. Check door for heat before opening

B. Wait in a safe area near the building exit

C. Extinguish visible fires coming from the roof

D. Stand in the center of the doorway while door is forced open

_____ 5. In which type of fire attack is water applied directly onto burning fuels until the fire is extinguished? (1013)

A. Direct attack

B. Indirect attack

C. Offensive attack

D. Defensive attack

_____ 6. In structures equipped with standpipe systems, the ___ will determine the method of fire attack. (1016)

A. location of the fire

B. number of exposures

C. location of the standpipe

D. number of hoselines available

_____ 7. Which of the following is an example of exterior exposure protection? (1022)

A. Closing doors or windows

B. Removal of endangered persons

C. Proper use of tactical ventilation

D. Use of fire-rated walls and doors

_____ 8. Which alternative sources of power can be controlled by simply shutting them off? (1024)
   A. Solar panels
   B. Wind turbines
   C. Fuel-powered generators
   D. Hybrid-powered generators

_____ 9. Which of the following gases is lighter than air so it rises and diffuses in the open? (1025)
   A. Ethanol
   B. Propane
   C. Natural gas
   D. Liquefied petroleum gas

_____ 10. Once in place, a master stream device can be operated by how many firefighters? (1030)
   A. One
   B. Two
   C. Three
   D. Four

_____ 11. Which of the following guidelines should be used at rescues in commercial high-voltage installations? (1034)
   A. Entrants should search with the back of the hand.
   B. Entry teams must wear haz mat suits and full PPE.
   C. Entry personnel must wear a tag line monitored by the front firefighter.
   D. Rescue operations should only be performed if three or more victims are trapped.

_____ 12. Which of the following is a guideline for electrical emergencies? (1036)
   A. Use fog-streams with at least 50 psi (345 kPa) nozzle pressure
   B. Do not start any vehicle or apparatus within the vicinity of power lines
   C. Do not use solid or straight streams on fires in energized electrical equipment
   D. Stay at least 20 feet (6 m) away from power lines when raising or lowering ground ladders

_____ 13. At a vehicle incident, which guidelines should be followed for protecting the scene from vehicular traffic? (1038)
   A. Department of Transportation (DOT)
   B. National Fire Protection Association (NFPA)
   C. Occupational Safety and Health Administration (OSHA)
   D. National Institute of Occupational Safety and Health (NIOSH)

_____ 14. At vehicle fire attacks, deploy an attack hoseline that will provide a minimum ___ gpm (L/min) flow rate. (1039)

A. 45 (170)

B. 55 (208)

C. 75 (284)

D. 95 (380)

_____ 15. At an incident involving alternative fuels, park the apparatus a minimum of ___ feet (m) from the incident. (1043)

A. 50 (15)

B. 75 (23)

C. 100 (30)

D. 125 (38)

_____ 16. What is a goal at a fire involving stacked and piled materials? (1047)

A. Extinguish the fire immediately

B. Confine fire to pile or building of origin

C. Extinguish fire using least amount of water

D. Ensure that materials of greatest value are protected first

_____ 17. Which type of ground cover fire moves through tree tops of heavily forested areas? (1050)

A. Soil fire

B. Crown fire

C. Surface fire

D. Ground fire

_____ 18. Which ground cover fuels include needles, duff, and twigs? (1051)

A. Aerial fuels

B. Crown fuel

C. Surface fuels

D. Subsurface fuels

_____ 19. Which weather aspect has the most significant effect on dead fuels that only gain moisture from the surrounding air? (1051)

A. Wind

B. Temperature

C. Precipitation

D. Relative humidity

_____ 20. Which method used to attack ground cover fires is used at varying distances from the advancing fire? (1054)

A. Direct

B. Indirect

C. Offensive

D. Defensive

Short Answer

Write the correct answers on the lines provided.

1. A defensive attack is employed when what conditions are present at a structure fire? (1006-1007)

____

____

____

____

2. What factors contribute to basement fires? (1006-1007)

____

____

____

____

3. What are the four main uses of a master stream device? (1018)

____

____

____

____

4. List five locations in which Class C fires may occur? (1031)

____

____

____

____

____

5. What are three consequences of electrical shock? (1035)

____

____

____

6. What are three causes of ground cover fires? (1049)

____

____

____

7. List four of the Ten Standard Firefighting Orders. (1056)

____

____

____

____

Crossword Puzzle

Across

5. Hose of ¾-inch to 2 inches (20 mm to 50 mm) in diameter; used for fire fighting purposes

8. Covering any object in the immediate vicinity of the fire with water or foam

9. Extinguishing a fire by using both a direct and an indirect attack

10. Any of several petroleum products, such as propane or butane, stored under pressure as a liquid

11. A fire that is located in a remote part of the structure or hidden from view by objects in the compartment

Down

1. Any voltage in excess of 600 volts

2. Structure or separate part of the fireground to which a fire could spread

3. Physical configuration of the land or terrain

4. Toxic compound found in some older oil-filled electric transformers

6. Form of fire attack that involves directing fire streams toward the ceiling of a compartment in order to generate a large amount of steam in order to cool the compartment

7. A friction match with a large head capable of burning in a wind

10. Any voltage that is less than 600 volts and safe enough for domestic use, typically 120 volts or less

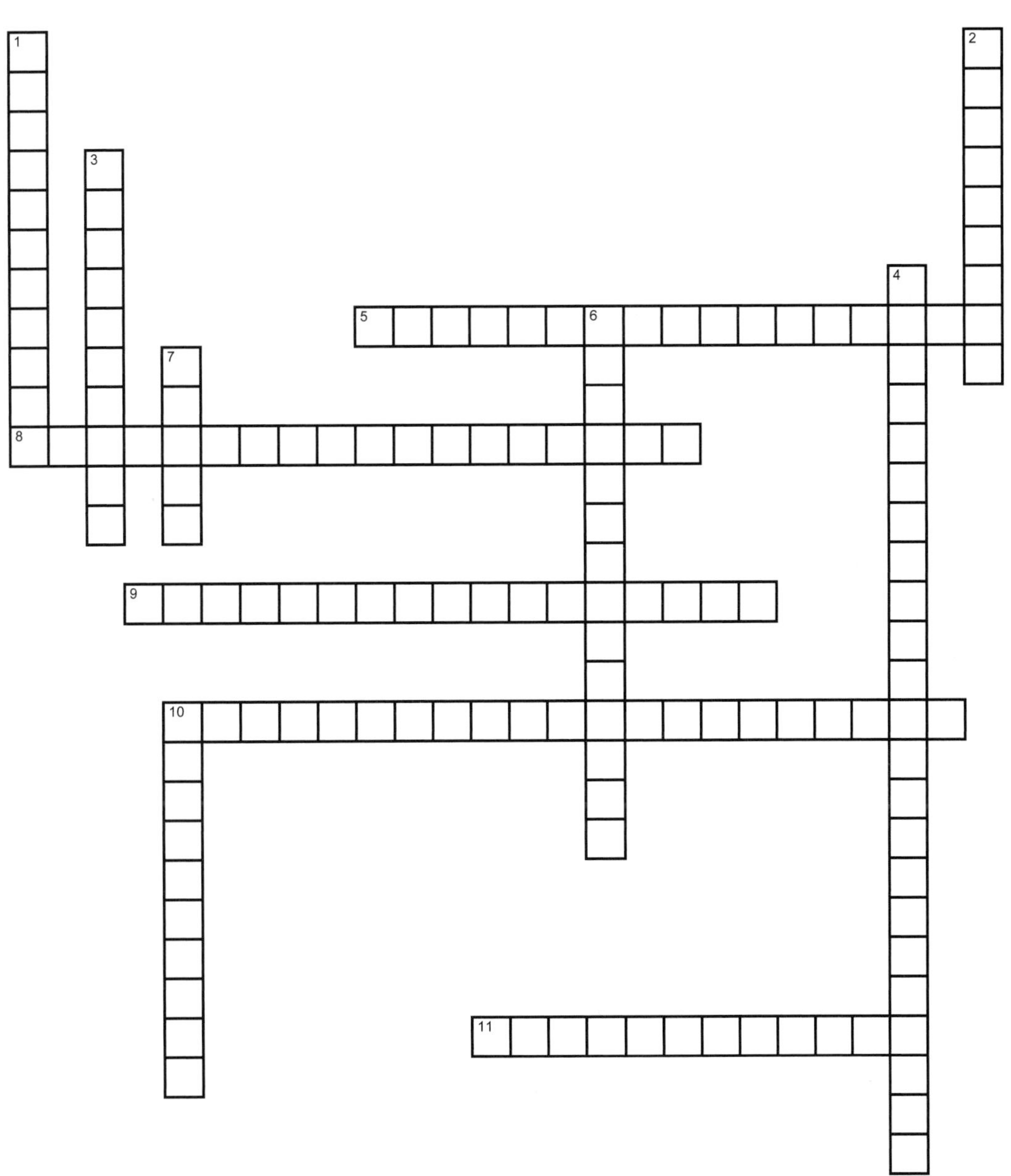
1
2
3
4
5
6
7
8
9
10
11

17

Terms

Write the definition of the terms below on the blanks provided.

1. **Blitz Attack (1062)** ____

____

2. **Total Flooding System (1072)** ____

____

True/False

Write True or False on the blanks provided; if False, write the correct statement on the lines provided.

________ 1. Open communication on the fireground means that each firefighter should vote on a task before it begins. (1058)

____

____

________ 2. A rapid intervention crew/team (RIC/RIT) may be assigned to other duties on the fireground, but these must be immediately stopped if deployment is needed. (1063)

____

____

________ 3. In a combat command situation the officer only performs duties as the Incident Commander (IC). (1065)

____

____

________ 4. Flammable liquids have a flashpoint of more than 100°F (38°C). (1068)

____

____

________ 5. A building site plan will show water supplies, protection system connections, and unit placement. (1071)

____

____

________ 6. The safe angle to approach a fire-involved pressurized storage tank is determined by wind direction. (1074)

____

____

________ 7. Bulk transportation vehicle fire extinguishment techniques are similar to those in flammable fuel storage facilities. (1075)

____

____

Fill in the Blank

Write the correct answer on the blanks provided.

1. Safety precautions at flammable/combustible liquid fire incidents require situational awareness of specific actions that may need to be avoided. For example, because protective clothing can absorb fuel in wicking action, firefighters should avoid standing in pools of ______________ or ______________ contaminated with fuel ______________. (1069)

2. Unburned vapors are heavier than air and may form pools of gas in low areas. To avoid this hazard firefighters should not extinguish liquids burning around ______________ until the leak is controlled. (1069)

3. A relief valve can provide important information to a firefighter. Any increase in ______________ from the relief valve may indicate the vessel is overheating or that rupture is imminent. (1070)

4. It is important to recognize conditions created when liquid is heated in a closed container. Firefighters must know that the change from liquid to gas ______________ internal pressure of a vessel. (1070)

5. Non-water-based fixed systems are found in industrial occupancies, aircraft hangers and maintenance facilities, and large cargo vessels. When active these systems will either fill the compartment with an ______________ or ______________ to suppress the fire. (1072)

Identification

Identify the search priority areas in the image on the lines provided.

Search Priorities (1062)

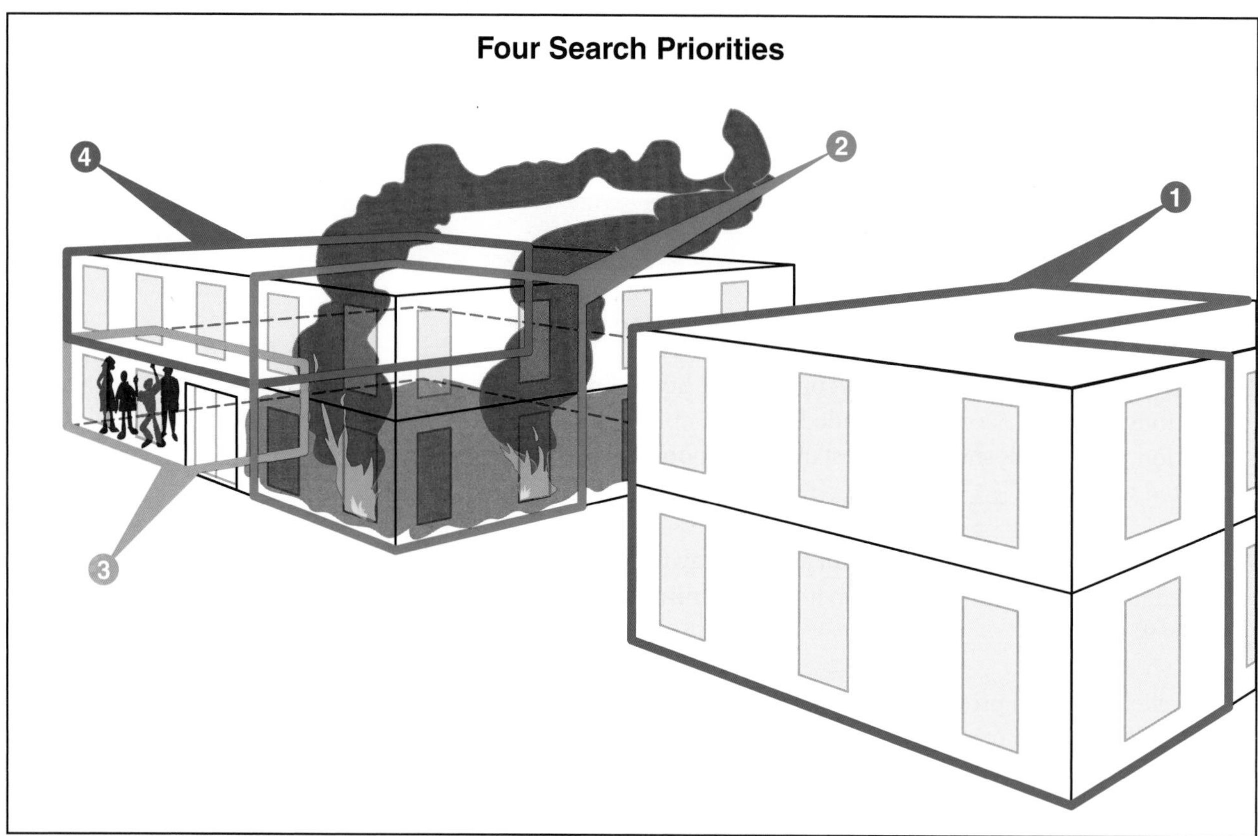

1. ______________________________

2. ______________________________

3. ______________________________

4. ______________________________

Matching

Write the correct answers on the blanks provided.

Fireground Roles and Responsibilities

Match the description with the fireground role listed. Each choice will be used once.

_________ 1. The goal of this role is to locate and assist firefighters that are trapped, lost, or incapacitated during operations (1063)

_________ 2. This role will first make sure there is an adequate water supply established to the fireground before finishing other tasks such as deploying additional hoseline or connecting to a hydrant to support deployed lines (1060-1061)

_________ 3. This role may choose to assume another role if the incident is well organized and reasonable progress has been made toward incident stabilization (1064)

_________ 4. This role performs the tasks of establishing Command, making initial size-up, and communicating the situation to the communication center and other units (1058-1060)

_________ 5. This tasks for this role are determined by the situation and may include checking the outside of a building for victims needing immediate rescue or forcing entry for simultaneous interior fire attack/search and rescue operations (1061-1062)

A. First-arriving engine company

B. Second-arriving engine company

C. Fireground support company

D. Rapid intervention crew/team (RIC/RIT)

E. Chief Officer

Command Options

Match the description with the type of command option listed. Each choice will be used once.

_________ 1. This option is used when it is necessary to take immediate action to save a life or stabilize the situation (1064-1065)

_________ 2. This option is exercised when the problem is not obvious to the first-arriving unit (1064)

_________ 3. This option is performed either face-to-face or over the radio; it cannot be done if one firefighter is not on scene (1066-1068)

_________ 4. This option is chosen based on the nature and scope of the incident; it is required in combat or formal command situations (1065-1066)

A. Nothing showing

B. Fast-attack

C. Name incident and establish Incident Command Post

D. Transferring Command

Multiple Choice

Write the correct answers on the blanks provided.

_____ 1. Which of the following BEST describes why a Firefighter II should listen to the observations of other firefighters with you on the fireground? (1058)

A. They have a better idea of how to command the situation.

B. They are allowed to vote on tasks before completing them.

C. They make the final decisions based on the input of those on scene.

D. They have a different physical point of view and may see something you do not.

_____ 2. Which of the following BEST describes what information must be communicated when transferring Command? (1066)

A. Name of incident, incident status, and safety considerations

B. Incident start time, incident status, and number of personnel on scene

C. Name of incident, location of all apparatus, and rank of officer being replaced

D. Incident location, progress to objectives, and amount of media presence on scene

_____ 3. Which of the following is an atmospheric, physical hazard that can be expected at a fire in an underground space? (1067)

A. Command post location

B. Materials stored on scene

C. Flammable gases and vapors

D. Limited relief for scene workers

_____ 4. Which of the following BEST describes the result of indirectly attacking a fire in an underground space? (1068)

A. Hose equipment will malfunction more frequently

B. Hose equipment will require replacement faster due to heat

C. Firefighters will be able to last longer between rehab sessions

D. Firefighters may consume air faster due to difficulties venting heat from space

_____ 5. Which of the following BEST describes the most common cause of a BLEVE? (1070)

A. Sparks from tools in the area

B. Mechanical damage to the tank

C. Flames contact tank shell below liquid level

D. Insufficient water is applied to keep tank shell cool

_____ 6. In a fixed protection system, connecting a pumper to the fire department connection will help: (1071)

A. help locate system connections.

B. maintain constant pressure on the system.

C. remove sprinkler stops that block water flow.

D. prevent the system from closing prematurely.

_____ 7. What type of fixed protection system is installed where large quantities of Class B flammable/combustible liquids are stored and used? (1072)

A. Foam

B. Standpipe

C. Non-water-based

D. Automatic sprinkler

_____ 8. Which of the following BEST describes where water should be applied when used as a cooling agent to protect exposures? (1073)

A. In the direction that will sweep fuel into sewers

B. Side to side to sweep fuel toward desired location

C. Above level of contained liquid on burning storage tanks

D. Below level of contained liquid on burning storage tanks

_____ 9. Which of the following BEST describes a hazard created during bulk transport vehicle fires? (1075)

A. Bills of lading may be misplaced

B. Traffic may require the use of road flares

C. The flammable load could shift if the tires fail

D. Location may be isolated from other civilian occupancies

Short Answer

Write the correct answers on the blanks provided.

1. When may the two-in two-out rule be amended? (1059)

____

____

____

____

2. What are the first concerns at flammable gas incidents? (1076)

____

____

____

____

Chapter 18

Loss Control

Firefighter I

Terms

Write the definition of the terms below on the blanks provided.

1. **Loss Control (1104)** ____________________

2. **Primary Damage (1104)** ____________________

3. **Secondary Damage (1104)** ____________________

4. **Salvage (1104)** ____________________

5. **Overhaul (1104)** ____________________

6. **Scupper (1109)** ____________________

7. **Carryall (1111)** ____________________

8. **Thermal Imager (1118)** ____________________

True/False

Write True or False on the blanks provided; if False, write the correct statement on the lines provided.

_______ 1. Minimizing losses to property is a sign of firefighter professionalism. (1104)

_______ 2. The preincident plan includes all means of evacuating or protecting building occupants during a fire. (1104)

_______ 3. Contents removed from a structure during salvage procedures should be protected from theft and vandalism once the fire has been extinguished. (1107)

_______ 4. A salvage cover may need to be placed over a bed before putting other household items on it. (1108)

_______ 5. Properly cleaned, dried, and repaired salvage covers have longer service lives. (1109)

_______ 6. Chalk is used to mark any holes on vinyl salvage covers. (1110)

_______ 7. Carryalls are devices used to remove water from basements or elevator shafts. (1111)

_________ 8. A rolled salvage cover is typically carried on the shoulder or under the arm. (1113)

____

____

_________ 9. A folded salvage cover for a two-firefighter spread can easily be used for a one-firefighter spread. (1114)

____

____

_________ 10. A hoseline is used to construct a catchall. (1116)

____

____

_________ 11. Covering openings is critical to prevent further damage to property by weather and trespassers. (1116)

____

____

_________ 12. Determining the cause of the fire is an operation performed during overhaul. (1118)

____

____

_________ 13. The first consideration before beginning overhaul is safety. (1119)

____

____

_________ 14. Ceilings may be opened from below during overhaul with a pike pole. (1122)

____

____

Fill in the Blank

Write the correct answer on the blanks provided.

1. Permitting canvas salvage covers to dry when dirty is not good as _______________ and _______________ stains can rot canvas. (1109)

2. Canvas salvage covers should be completely clean and dry before being folded and stored on the apparatus to prevent _______________ or _______________. (1109)

3. The most convenient way to carry a folded salvage cover is on the shoulder with open edges next to the _______________. (1114)

4. Covering openings created during salvage is critical to prevent further damage to property by _______________ or _______________. (1116)

5. _______________ consists of activities conducted once the main body of fire has been extinguished. (1118)

6. _______________ the premises at the scene of the fire incident is the first step in the overhaul plan. (1119)

Identification

Identify the following items on the lines provided.

Salvage Covers and Equipment (1109-1115)

Identify the salvage covers and loss control equipment in the images below.

1. _______________________________

2. ______________________________

3. ______________________________

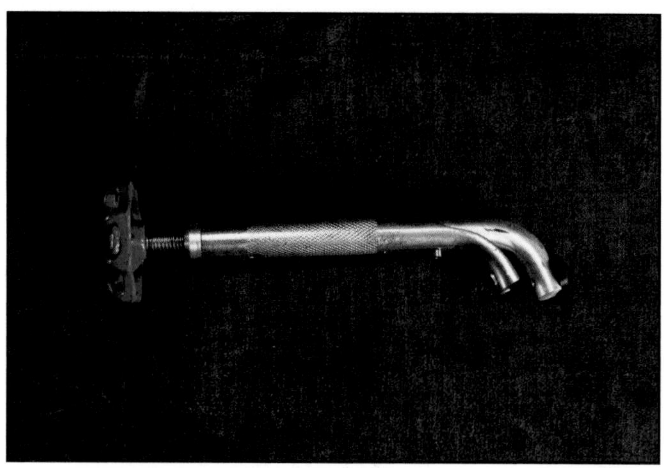

5. ______________________________

4. ______________________

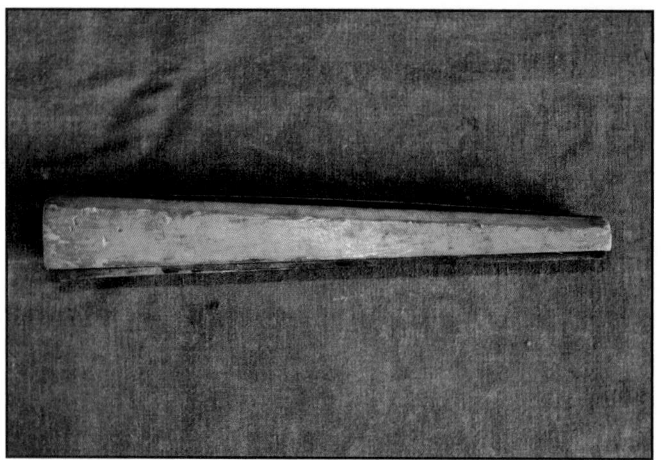

6. ______________________________

7. ______________________

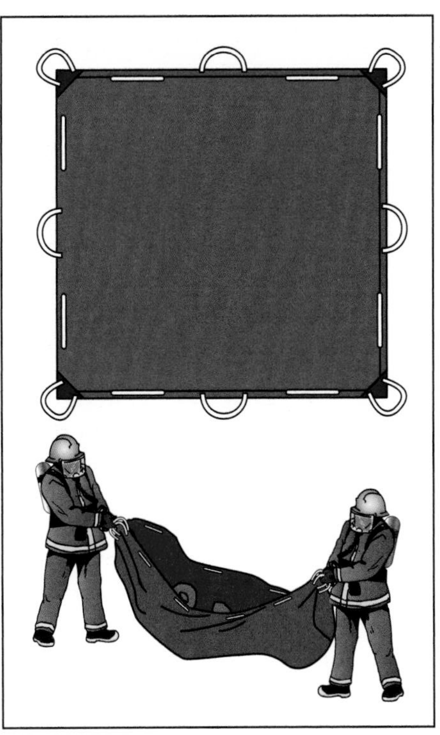

8. ______________________________

9. ____

Matching

Write the correct answers on the blanks provided.

Improvising with Salvage Covers
Match the description with the salvage cover improvisation listed. Answers may be used more than once.

_____ 1. This improvisation is used when objects are too large to be covered by a single cover. (1116)

_____ 2. This improvisation is constructed on the floor below fire fighting operations and used to drain runoff out of the structure's windows or doors. (1114)

_____ 3. Placed on floor to hold small amounts of water, this improvisation can hold several hundred gallons (liters) of water. (1116)

_____ 4. Constructed from salvage covers, this improvisation is used to catch as much water as possible by putting it into position as soon as possible even if the sides are not uniformly rolled. (1116)

_____ 5. Use of this improvisation is one of the most practical methods of removing water coming through the ceiling from upper floors. (1114)

_____ 6. Using disposable rolled plastic sheeting cut to size, as needed, this improvisation saves time and property. (1116)

A. Water chute
B. Catchall
C. Spliced covers

Multiple Choice

Write the correct answers on the blanks provided.

_____ 1. Which of the following refers to damage caused by suppression activities? (1104)
A. Initial damage
B. Primary damage
C. Secondary damage
D. Postincident damage

_____ 2. How should household furnishings be grouped when arranging for salvage operations? (1108)
A. In many small piles
B. Lined around the edges of the room
C. Stacked at one end of the room near a window
D. On dry surfaces not near where debris for disposal is being collected

_____ 3. How should commercial occupancies' stock be stored so it is less vulnerable to water damage? (1108)

A. On skids or pallets
B. In large plastic tubs
C. Covered by plastic sheeting
D. Shrink-wrapped with black plastic

_____ 4. Vinyl synthetic salvage covers have which of the following characteristics? (1109)

A. Expensive
B. Lightweight
C. Difficult to handle
D. To be used indoors only

_____ 5. Which of the following statements is MOST accurate about synthetic salvage covers? (1110)

A. Require less maintenance than canvas salvage covers
B. Require more maintenance than canvas salvage covers
C. Have the same maintenance requirements as canvas salvage covers
D. Have more maintenance initially but over time require less maintenance than canvas salvage covers

_____ 6. An automatic sprinkler kit is made up of tools used to: (1110)

A. stop the flow of water from an open sprinkler.
B. begin the flow of water from a closed sprinkler.
C. help extinguish small fires in commercial structures only.
D. work in tandem with nozzle hoses used to extinguish a fire.

_____ 7. Which of the following are used to protect floor coverings from unintentional damage caused by firefighters' boots and equipment during fire suppression operations? (1111)

A. Scuppers
B. Carryalls
C. Floor runners
D. Portable pumps

_____ 8. Which of the following cannot be driven into walls or framing but must have a horizontal ledge from which to hang? (1112)

A. C-hooks
B. J-hooks
C. S-hooks
D. U-hooks

_____ 9. Which of the following is the most common method for two firefighters to deploy a large salvage cover? (1114)

A. Tent pitch
B. Balloon throw
C. Change-up pitch
D. Fold and flip throw

_____ 10. If the fire investigator is on scene, he/she should be involved in the planning and supervising of overhaul activities to: (1118)

A. avoid disturbing potential evidence needed to determine fire cause.
B. search for and extinguish any hidden or remaining fire in the structure.
C. cover property to protect it from exposure during firefighting operations.
D. account for all firefighting personnel needed to complete the investigation.

_____ 11. Which of the following must be a routine part of the overhaul process? (1119)

A. Estimating clean-up costs
B. Wearing loose, comfortable clothing
C. Providing needed tools and equipment
D. Determining appropriate mode of fire attack

_____ 12. Which of the following is a safety consideration during overhaul operations? (1120)

A. Continue to work in teams of two or more
B. Disconnect all attack lines used in initial operations
C. Wear loose, comfortable clothing to avoid overheating
D. Maintain a RIC/RIT until overhaul operations are well underway

_____ 13. Which of the following is an indicator of a possible hidden fire? (1121)

A. Popping or cracking of fire burning
B. Absence of sound from a particular area
C. Doors that have become partially or completely open
D. Areas that appear to be visually unaffected by the fire

_____ 14. Fire may extend to other areas of a structure, so firefighters must determine if the fire traveled through concealed wall spaces or: (1121)

A. sealed pipe chases.
B. unsealed pipe chases.
C. heavily insulated floors.
D. combustible roofs or cornices.

_____ 15. Which of the following statements about insulation is MOST accurate? (1121)

A. Usually it is necessary to remove insulation material to extinguish the fire in it.

B. Insulation materials are generally fire-retardant and cannot harbor hidden fires.

C. Insulation materials are generally self-extinguishing and are not a hidden fire concern.

D. Usually the material does not need to be removed and the fire can be extinguished in it in the structure.

_____ 16. Which of the following methods is the MOST effective way to extinguish small burning objects uncovered during overhaul? (1122)

A. Drench them with hose streams

B. Cover them with salvage covers

C. Set them outside to self-extinguish

D. Submerge them in containers of water

_____ 17. Use of wetting agents such as Class A foam: (1122)

A. can cause fires to reignite.

B. should not be considered during overhaul.

C. is valuable when extinguishing hidden fires.

D. can be used during overhaul, but not on upholstery.

_____ 18. If there is a discrepancy between a thermal imager and signs of fire in a concealed space: (1123)

A. the space should be opened up and inspected visually.

B. the thermal imager should be checked for malfunction.

C. traditional methods to reveal hidden fire should not be used.

D. charged fire hoses should be brought in to thoroughly douse the concealed space.

Short Answer

Write the correct answers on the lines provided.

1. Name three items that might be considered high-value contents? (1106)

____

____

____

2. List two factors to consider when choosing particular salvage procedures. (1107)

____

____

3. Name two things that should be done when protecting contents in place if the floor covering is a removable rug? (1108)

4. Name two challenges that become present with high-piled stock in a commercial occupancy. (1108)

5. Name two salvage procedures that remove large quantities of water during loss control. (1108-1109)

Scenario

Answer the following questions based on the scenarios below.

Scenario 1

A fire in a single story, large area warehouse protected by an automatic sprinkler system has been controlled by the system and by firefighters using an offensive strategy. You and your crew are assigned to protect the contents stored on shelving from water damage.

1. What is the first action that must be taken to limit further damage to the contents?

2. What action can be taken to prevent the collapse of water-soaked contents stored on shelves?

3. How can large quantities of water be removed from the building?

4. If building components are not available to remove water, what can firefighters construct to remove the water?

Scenario 2

A fire in a two-story wood-frame residential structure has been extinguished. You and your crew have been assigned the task of overhauling one portion of the structure.

1. What is the first consideration before beginning overhaul?

2. What should be monitored for prior to removing respiratory protection (SCBA)?

3. What other safety hazards should be considered during overhaul?

4. What are two important factors that will affect the structural integrity of the building?

5. When looking for hidden fires, what indicators should be used?

6. At what point in the structure should the overhaul process begin?

Crossword Puzzle

Across

2. Waterproof carrier used to carry and catch debris or used as a water sump basin for immersing small burning objects
5. Methods and operating procedures by which firefighters attempt to save property and reduce further damage from water, smoke, heat, and exposure during or immediately after a fire
6. Damage caused by or resulting from those actions taken to fight a fire and leaving property unprotected

Down

1. Damage caused by a fire itself and not by actions taken to fight the fire
3. Practice of minimizing damage and providing customer service through effective mitigation and recovery efforts before, during, and after an incident
4. Operations conducted once the main body of fire has been extinguished; consists of searching for and extinguishing hidden or remaining fire, placing the building and its contents in a safe condition, determining the cause of the fire, and recognizing and preserving evidence of arson

Chapter 19

Fire Origin and Cause Determination

Terms

Write the definition of the terms below on the blanks provided.

1. **Area of Origin (1145)** ____________________

   ____

2. **Point of Origin (1145)** ____________________

   ____

3. **Fire Cause (1146)** ____________________

   ____

4. **Arson (1146)** ____________________

   ____

5. **Chain of Custody (1146)** ____________________

   ____

6. **Fire Pattern (1147)** ____________________

   ____

7. **Competent Ignition Source (1153)** ____________________

   ____

8. **Ignition Sequence (1153)** ____________________

   ____

9. **Trailer (1157)** ____________________

   ____

10. **Incendiary Device (1158)** ____________________

____

11. **Contamination (1163)** ____________________

____

12. **Spoliation (1164)** ____________________

____

True/False

Write True or False on the blanks provided; if False, write the correct statement on the lines provided.

_____ 1. It can be assumed that potentially lethal concentrations of unburned gases such as carbon monoxide (CO) and hydrogen cyanide (HCN) are not present at an area of origin. (1145-1146)

____

____

_____ 2. Move all debris when searching with or without orders to do so. (1146)

____

____

_____ 3. Upward movement of heat causes less damage to floors than ceilings. (1148)

____

____

_____ 4. Multiple areas of origin may not indicate intentionally set fires. (1149)

____

____

_____ 5. When burning on flat ground with a consistent fuel source and no wind, fire burns in equal directions. (1150)

____

____

_______ 6. During rescue operations, firefighters should cut the door post on a hybrid or electric car. (1152)

____

____

_______ 7. The absence of an obvious ignition source may help eliminate some causes and allow investigation to focus on others. (1156)

____

____

_______ 8. When observing conditions, look for obsolete equipment or inventory. (1159)

____

____

_______ 9. All firefighters can determine what is and is not evidence. (1159)

____

____

_______ 10. Perimeters should only be recognizable by firefighters. (1160)

____

____

_______ 11. Evidence must remain undisturbed except when absolutely necessary for extinguishment of fire. (1162)

____

____

Matching

Write the correct answers on the blanks provided.

Fire Cause Classifications

Match the fire cause with the correct classification. Answers will be used more than once.

______	1. Arson crimes (1154)	A. Accidental
______	2. Earthquakes (1154)	B. Natural
______	3. Flammable vapors (1154)	C. Incendiary
______	4. Lightning strikes (1154)	D. Undetermined
______	5. Overloaded electrical circuits (1154)	
______	6. Unknown ignition sources (1154-1155)	

Multiple Choice

Write the correct answers on the blanks provided.

_____ 1. Which of the following statements is MOST accurate about the area of origin? (1146)
- A. The debris will contain an indication of fire cause.
- B. It is the precise location of where the fire began.
- C. It contains the least amount of damage and debris.
- D. The point of origin will not be able to be determined.

_____ 2. Protecting the scene and delaying overhaul operations should be done when: (1147)
- A. conducting search operations.
- B. the origin has been determined.
- C. origin cannot be accurately determined.
- D. starting operations to determine the fire origin.

_____ 3. Which of the following statements is MOST accurate about floor charring? (1148)
- A. It can be caused by flashover
- B. It will also appear on the ceiling
- C. It will appear farthest away from the point of origin
- D. It is scattered and appears uneven across doors and objects

_____ 4. Terrain/topography affects the rate and direction of spread in ___ fires. (1150)

A. interior

B. exterior

C. vehicle

D. structure

_____ 5. Which of the following can cause a fire in a structure? (1153-1154)

A. Hydraulic systems

B. Plumbing systems

C. Pneumatic systems

D. Air-conditioning systems

_____ 6. Which of the following is NOT a type of fire cause classification? (1154)

A. Natural

B. Incendiary

C. Unintentional

D. Undetermined

_____ 7. Which type of fire cause is deliberately set? (1154)

A. Natural

B. Incendiary

C. Unintentional

D. Undetermined

_____ 8. Which of the following would be additional information to provide to fire investigators? (1157)

A. Topography

B. Staffing level

C. Time of arrival

D. Basic fire behavior

_____ 9. Which of the following is an obstacle that could hinder firefighting? (1158)

A. Sliding windows

B. Doors nailed shut

C. Doorways left open

D. Electricity being cut off

_____ 10. Which of the following is a way to establish perimeters? (1160)

A. Use bystanders to control access into the boundaries

B. Always set up perimeters based on explosion distance

C. Make barriers so they are only visible to a few individuals at a time

D. Ensure that initial perimeters are larger than necessary for investigations

_____ 11. Limiting access to a scene also provides ___ for firefighters. (1162)
- A. harm
- B. safety
- C. restrictions
- D. consequences

_____ 12. Which of the following can occur even if a scene is secured? (1162)
- A. Limitation
- B. Restriction
- C. Contamination
- D. Detoxification

_____ 13. Which of the following is defined as evidence that is destroyed, damage, altered, or otherwise not preserved? (1164)
- A. Spoliation
- B. Alteration
- C. Limitation
- D. Detoxification

Short Answer

Write the correct answers on the lines provided.

1. What are the critical parts to the overall success of the finding the area of origin? (1146)

____

____

____

2. What affects the rate and direction of spread in exterior fires? (1150)

____

____

____

____

____

____

____

3. What information should a firefighter provide to a fire investigator? (1156)

4. List the guidelines for establishing a perimeter of proper size for both explosions and structure fires. (1160)

Crossword Puzzle

Across

2. Continuous changes of possession of physical evidence that must be established in court to admit such material into evidence
4. The sequence of events that allow the ignition source and the material first ignited to come together
7. Term that refers to evidence that is destroyed, damaged, altered, or otherwise not preserved by someone who has responsibility for the evidence
8. Combustible material, such as rolled rags, blankets, newspapers, or flammable liquid, often used in intentionally set fires in order to spread fire from one area to other points or areas
9. Exact physical location where the heat source and fuel come in contact with each other and a fire begins
11. A competent ignition source will have sufficient temperature and energy and be in contact with the fuel long enough to raise it to its ignition temperature

Down

1. General term referring to anything that can taint physical evidence
3. The general location (room or area) where the ignition source and the material first ignited actually came together for the first time
5. The apparent and obvious design of burned material and the burning path of travel from a point of fire origin
6. Crime of willfully, maliciously, and intentionally starting an incendiary fire or causing an explosion to destroy one's property or the property of another
10. History of the fire, beginning when the ignition source and the first fuel ignited meet at the area of origin, and proceeding through the entire duration of fire spread through the scene
12. Material or chemicals designed and used to start a fire

1
2
3
4
5
6
7
8
9
10
11
12

19

Terms

Write the definition of the terms below on the blanks provided.

1. **Direct Evidence (1165)** ______________________________

____

2. **Circumstantial evidence (1165)** ______________________________

____

3. **Physical evidence (1165)** ______________________________

____

4. **Exigent Circumstances (1171)** ______________________________

____

Firefighter II

True/False

Write True or False on the blanks provided; if False, write the correct statement on the lines provided.

______ 1. Circumstantial evidence is not as valuable as direct evidence. (1165)

____

____

______ 2. Alarm clocks are often used as timing devices. (1167)

____

____

______ 3. Matches are not always consumed by a fire. (1168)

____

____

______ 4. Guidelines for requesting assistance of personnel vary by jurisdictions and according to the nature of the incident. (1169)

____

____

_______ 5. Public statements will be made after fire investigator and officer in charge have agreed on fire cause. (1170)

____

____

_______ 6. The responsibility for determining fire cause lies only with the insurance investigator. (1170)

____

____

_______ 7. Adjusters and arson investigators may compare their findings during an investigation. (1171)

____

____

_______ 8. Responding to an emergency grants firefighters the right to enter and remain on the premises. (1171)

____

____

Matching

Write the correct answers on the blanks provided.

Roles and Responsibilities

Match the correct responsibility with the best role. Answers will be used more than once.

_______ 1. Takes mental notes (1169)
_______ 2. Could be a peace officer (1170)
_______ 3. Performs careful overhaul (1170)
_______ 4. Conducts detailed analysis (1170)
_______ 5. Determines amount of loss (1170)
_______ 6. Makes investigation after fire is out (1170)
_______ 7. Recognizes and collects important information (1169)

A. Firefighter
B. Fire investigator
C. Insurance investigator

Multiple Choice

Write the correct answers on the blanks provided.

_____ 1. A fire investigator decides what is ___ as evidence. (1167)
- A. cleared
- B. cleaned
- C. censored
- D. collected

_____ 2. Which of the following is used to spread fire from one area to another? (1167)
- A. Glass
- B. Bottles
- C. Trailers
- D. Lighters

_____ 3. Properly trained firefighters should be able to recognize and collect important information during all the following EXCEPT: (1169)
- A. immediately upon arrival.
- B. while extinguishing a fire.
- C. when entering a structure.
- D. when reentering the scene.

_____ 4. Which of the following tasks may an insurance investigator be hired for? (1170)
- A. Help put out a fire in a structure
- B. Determine the number of fatalities
- C. Liability for fires involving property they insure
- D. Authorizing permission to reenter an incident scene

_____ 5. Which of the following normally results in contradictory conclusions? (1171)
- A. Differing investigative methodologies or oversight
- B. Not using the same fire investigators for every fire
- C. Comparing fires between different two structures
- D. Collecting everything from the scene as evidence

_____ 6. Location and collection of evidence is based on: (1171)
- A. right of entry.
- B. a variety of laws.
- C. chain of custody.
- D. the amount of damage.

_____ 7. Which of the following is NOT needed for right of entry during search and seizure? (1171)

A. A warrant

B. Consent from the owner

C. Mitigating an emergency

D. Document stating origin and cause

Short Answer

Write the correct answers on the lines provided.

1. What are the three primary categories of evidence? (1165)

____

____

____

2. What should a firefighter provide when assisting an investigator? (1170)

____

____

____

3. What are the responsibilities of an insurance adjuster? (1170-1171)

____

____

____

____

____

4. What legal issues impact collection of evidence during a fire investigation? (1171)

____

____

____

____

____

Chapter 20

Fire Protection Systems

Terms

Write the definition of the terms below on the blanks provided.

1. **Fire Protection System (1178)** ____

____

2. **Fire Alarm Control Panel (FACP) (1178)** ____

____

3. **Annunciator Panel (1178)** ____

____

4. **Fire Command Center (1181)** ____

____

5. **Protected Premises System (1182)** ____

____

6. **Auxiliary Alarm System (1184)** ____

____

7. **Local Energy System (1184)** ____

____

8. **Shunt Systems (1184)** ____

____

9. **Proprietary Alarm System (1184)** ____

____

10. **Central Station System (1184)** ____

____

11. **Remote Receiving System (1184)** ____

____

12. **Alarm-Initiating Device (1185)** ____

____

13. **Manual Pull Station (1185)** ____

____

14. **Heat Detector (1185)** ____

____

15. **Fusible Link (1186)** ____

____

16. **Frangible Bulb (1186)** ____

____

17. **Rate-of-Rise Heat Detector (1188)** ____

____

18. **Smoke Detector (1190)** ____

____

19. **Smoke Alarm (1190)** ____

____

20. **Photoelectric Smoke Detector (1190)** ____

____

21. **Ionization Smoke Detector (1192)** ____

____

22. **Flame Detector (1193)** ______________________________

____

23. **Fire-Gas Detector (1194)** ______________________________

____

24. **Automatic Sprinkler System (1194)** ______________________________

____

25. **Sprinkler (1194)** ______________________________

____

26. **Riser (1196)** ______________________________

____

27. **Feed Main (1196)** ______________________________

____

28. **Cross Main (1196)** ______________________________

____

29. **Chemical Pellet (1197)** ______________________________

____

30. **Deflector (1198)** ______________________________

____

31. **Indicating Valve (1200)** ______________________________

____

32. **Drain Valve (1201)** ______________________________

____

33. **Alarm Check Valve (1201)** ______________________________

____

34. **Retard Chamber (1201)** ______________________________

35. **Waterflow Device (1202)** ______________________________

36. **Check Valve (1203)** ______________________________

37. **Wet-Pipe Sprinkler System (1204)** ______________________________

38. **Dry-Pipe Sprinkler System (1204)** ______________________________

39. **Deluge Sprinkler System (1205)** ______________________________

40. **Deluge Valve (1205)** ______________________________

41. **Preaction Sprinkler System (1207)** ______________________________

42. **Standpipe System (1209)** ______________________________

43. **House Line (1210)** ______________________________

44. **Smoke Management System (1213)** ______________________________

45. **Firefighter's Smoke Control Station (FSCS) (1215)** ______________________________

____

True/False

Write True or False on the blanks provided; if False, write the correct statement on the lines provided.

_______ 1. An alarm signal must be activated if the primary power source to the alarm system is interrupted. (1178)

____

____

_______ 2. A protected premises alarm signaling system is monitored by responders at a remote receiving point. (1182)

____

____

_______ 3. A supervising station alarm system continuously monitors a remote location. (1183)

____

____

_______ 4. Fixed-temperature heat detectors are most prone to false activations. (1186)

____

____

_______ 5. Fusible links and frangible bulbs in heat detectors do not automatically reset after activation. (1186)

____

____

_______ 6. A heat detector can initiate an alarm more quickly than a smoke detector. (1190)

____

____

_______ 7. Flame detectors are among the fastest detectors to respond to fires. (1193)

_______ 8. Sprinkler systems are designed to discharge enough water to make firefighter response unnecessary. (1194)

_______ 9. Sprinkler systems are recognized as the most reliable of all fire protection devices. (1195)

_______ 10. Early-suppression fast-response (ESFR) sprinklers activate twice as fast as traditional sprinklers. (1197)

Fill in the Blank

Write the correct answer on the blanks provided.

1. Fire alarm systems are important life-safety components of fire protection systems. Fire alarm systems provide notification of an emergency condition to _______________, and possibly to a local response organization. (1178)

2. NFPA® standards specify a minimum design area that should be used to calculate the sprinkler system. This minimum area is based on the maximum number of sprinklers that might be expected to activate at one time, and the assumption that only a _______________ of the sprinklers will activate during a fire. (1195)

3. Sprinkler systems enhance life safety by limiting products of combustion and preventing spread of a fire upward in multistory buildings, protecting building occupants. Sprinklers enhance life safety of firefighters by controlling fire in early stages, enhancing safety during _______________and fire suppression operations. (1195-1196)

4. Standpipe systems are valuable during _______________operations because they reduce the amount of hose needed to reach areas already controlled by sprinklers. (1209)

Matching

Write the correct answers on the blanks provided.

Alarm System Components

Match the component description with the alarm system component. Each choice may be used more than once.

_________ 1. When activated, sends signal to FACP (1180)

_________ 2. May control public address or mass notifications (1178)

_________ 3. May include building plans and system diagrams (1181)

_________ 4. Directly connected to power and fire alarm circuits (1178)

_________ 5. Categories include audible, visual, textual, and tactile (1180)

_________ 6. Consolidates fire protection system controls into one room (1181)

_________ 7. May include batteries with chargers and auxiliary generators (1178)

_________ 8. Contains electronics to control and monitor fire alarm system (1178)

_________ 9. May send signal to central alarm monitoring center or to fire department (1180)

_________ 10. Automatic types sense products of combustion or other hazardous conditions (1180)

_________ 11. Primary source usually obtained from building's main connection to local utility provider (1178)

_________ 12. Receives signals from alarm initiating devices, processes signals, produces output signals (1178)

A. Power supplies

B. Initiating devices

C. Fire command center

D. Notification appliances

E. Fire alarm control panel (FACP)

Protected Premises Alarm Signaling Systems

Match the description with the protected premises alarm signaling system. Each choice will be used more than once.

_______ 1. Simplest type of local alarm (1182-1183)

_______ 2. Only practical in small occupancies (1182-1183)

_______ 3. Responders can pinpoint specific initiating device activated (1183)

_______ 4. Allows for quick location and correction of system malfunctions (1183)

_______ 5. Not capable of identifying initiating device that triggered the alarm (1182-1183)

_______ 6. Enables responders to identify general location of alarm activation (1183)

_______ 7. Indicators on fire alarm control panel illuminate for a particular zone (1183)

_______ 8. Displays location of each initiating device on fire alarm control panel (1183)

A. Noncoded alarm 1182-1183
B. Zoned/annunciated alarm
C. Addressable alarm system

Firefighter II

Supervising Station Alarm Signaling Systems

Match the description with the supervising station alarm signaling system. Each choice may be used more than once.

_______ 1. Connected to municipal fire alarm system (1184)

_______ 2. Monitored by contracted services at the receiving point (1184)

_______ 3. System not connected through municipal alarm box system (1184)

_______ 4. Each building has own alarm system wired into common receiving point (1184)

_______ 5. May be a shunt system, a municipal circuit extending into protected property (1184)

_______ 6. Trained personnel staff the receiving station, summon fire department response (1184)

_______ 7. System connected to emergency services telecommunication through telephone line or via dedicated radio frequency (1184)

A. Proprietary system
B. Central station system
C. Auxiliary alarm system
D. Remote receiving system

Alarm-Initiating Devices

Match the method of activation with the alarm-initiating device. Each choice will be used only once.

_________ 1. Activated by light in ultraviolet or infrared spectrum (1193)

_________ 2. Activated by presence of smoke and other products of combustion (1190 -1193)

_________ 3. Activated manually, allows occupants to initiate fire signaling system (1185)

_________ 4. Activated by presence of gases released when fire burns in a confined space (1193-1194)

_________ 5. Activated when temperature in monitored area reaches predetermined threshold (1185-1190)

A. Pull station
B. Heat detector
C. Flame detector
D. Smoke detector
E. Fire-gas detector

Sprinkler Orientation Types

Match the description with the sprinkler orientation device. Each choice will be used only once.

_________ 1. Deflects spray downward in hemispherical pattern; cannot be inverted (1198)

_________ 2. Breaks water into circular pattern of small droplets directed downward; used where impractical to use upright (1198)

_________ 3. Discharges most of water to one side; used when necessary to install on wall at side of room, or to save space (1198)

_________ 4. Hidden by removable decorative cover that releases when exposed to specific heat level (1198)

_________ 5. Mounted in ceiling with body of sprinkler (including threaded shank) above plane of ceiling (1198)

_________ 6. Installed in housing within ceiling of compartment or space, all or part (other than threaded shank) in housing (1198)

_________ 7. Incorporates protective disk that shields heat-sensing element from water discharged from sprinklers above (1198)

A. Flush
B. In-Rack
C. Upright
D. Pendant
E. Side wall
F. Recessed
G. Concealed

Indicating Valve Types

Match the description with the indicating valve type. Each choice will be used only once.

_______ 1. Yoke on outside with threaded stem; threaded portion visible beyond the yoke when open, not when closed (1200)

_______ 2. Hollow metal post houses valve stem; a moveable plate with OPEN or SHUT is visible through a small glass window on the side of the housing (1200-1201)

_______ 3. Extends horizontally through wall with the target and valve operating nut outside of building (1201)

_______ 4. Uses a circular disk inside a flat plate on top of the valve housing; the disk is perpendicular to the plate when open, in line with the plate when closed (1201)

A. Post indicator valve (PIV)
B. Outside stem and yoke (OS&Y)
C. Wall post indicator valve (WPIV)
D. Post indicator valve assembly (PIVA)

Sprinkler System Applications

Match the description with the sprinkler system application. Each choice may be used more than once.

_______ 1. Contain water under pressure at all times (1204)

_______ 2. Use extinguishing agents other than water (1207)

_______ 3. Simplest type, generally requires little maintenance (1204)

_______ 4. All sprinklers open all the time (open-head sprinklers) (1205)

_______ 5. Valve controls water flow to discharge through all sprinklers (1205)

_______ 6. Used when it is especially important to prevent water damage (1207)

_______ 7. Used in locations where temperatures remain above 40°F (4°C) (1204)

_______ 8. Valve controls water flow to discharge when sprinklers are activated (1207)

_______ 9. May use accelerator or exhauster to redirect or expel air from system (1204-1205)

_______ 10. Normally, air pressure gauge reads at lower pressure than water pressure gauge (1204-1205)

_______ 11. Types include wet chemical, dry chemical, clean agent, carbon-dioxide and foam (1207)

_______ 12. System that employs deluge-type valve, fire-detection devices, and closed sprinklers (1207)

_______ 13. Connected to water supply, will immediately discharge water spray and activate alarm (1204)

_______ 14. Air or nitrogen under pressure replaces water in sprinkler piping above dry-pipe valve (1204-1205)

A. Deluge systems
B. Special systems
C. Dry-pipe systems
D. Wet-pipe systems
E. Preaction systems

Types of Standpipe Systems

Match the description with the standpipe system type. Each choice will be used only once.

_____ 1. Maintained full of water, but has no water supply (1212)

_____ 2. Contains air under pressure, water admitted to system upon opening of hose valve (1212)

_____ 3. Water-supply control valve is open and pressure maintained in the system at all times (1211)

_____ 4. Requires activation of control device; water admitted when dry-pipe valve is activated at hose station (1212)

_____ 5. Does not have permanent water supply, designed to have water only when system is supplied through fire department connection (1212)

A. Manual dry
B. Manual wet
C. Automatic dry
D. Automatic wet
E. Semiautomatic dry

Multiple Choice

Write the correct answers on the blanks provided.

_____ 1. Which of the following is NOT a possible function of the fire alarm control panel? (1178)

A. Detection of products of combustion
B. Operation of remote annunciator panel
C. Public address and mass notification systems
D. Operation of relays that capture and recall elevators

_____ 2. Which of the following statements about protected premises alarm systems is MOST accurate? (1182)

A. Protected premises alarms are only able to be activated manually.
B. Protected premises alarms have no provision for off-site reporting.
C. Protected premises alarms may be an extension of a municipal alarm circuit.
D. Protected premises alarms notify trained personnel at a remote receiving point.

_____ 3. Central station systems are monitored by: (1184)

A. community watch volunteers.
B. personnel employed by the building owner.
C. contracted services, such as alarm companies.
D. the local emergency services telecommunications center.

_____ 4. Which type of alarm-initiating device is activated when the temperature in a monitored area reaches a pre-determined threshold? (1185)

A. Heat detector
B. Flame detector
C. Smoke detector
D. Fire-gas detector

_____ 5. Which of the following is NOT an activation mechanism of fixed temperature heat detector? (1186)

A. Melting of heated material
B. Expansion of heated material
C. Changes in resistance of heated material
D. Changes in radioactive emissions of heated material

_____ 6. Which type of heat detector activates when solder melts, allowing a spring-operated contact to close, completing a circuit? (1186)

A. Bimetallic
B. Fusible link
C. Frangible bulb
D. Continuous line

_____ 7. Which type of heat detector is activated by liquid expanding to break a glass vial and allow contacts to complete a circuit? (1186-1187)

A. Bimetallic
B. Fusible link
C. Frangible bulb
D. Continuous line

_____ 8. Which type of heat detector detects heat over a linear line parallel to the detector? (1187)

A. Bimetallic detector
B. Infrared wave detector
C. Continuous line detector
D. Rate-compensated detector

_____ 9. How is a cable continuous line heat detector activated? (1187)

A. Heat causes air in a sealed tube to expand; the change in pressure activates an alarm circuit.
B. A system of electronic thermistors produces a change in electrical resistance when heated; change either closes or opens a circuit.
C. Two metals with different rates of thermal expansion are bonded together; heat causes the bonded metals to arch and complete a circuit.
D. Heat causes insulating material in the cable to lose electrical resistance, the current flow increases, and a signal is transmitted to the fire alarm control panel.

_____ 10. How is a bimetallic heat detector activated? (1187)

A. A solder pellet holds two metal strips apart; when heated, the solder melts, allowing the strips to touch and complete a circuit.

B. Two metal strips are held together with solder; when heated, the solder melts, allowing the strips to touch and complete a circuit

C. Two metals with different rates of thermal expansion are bonded together; heat causes the bonded metals to arch and make or break a circuit.

D. Two insulated metal wires are bundled into an outer covering; heat causes the insulation to melt, allowing the wires to touch and complete a circuit.

_____ 11. Which of the following statements BEST describes rate-of-rise heat detectors? (1188)

A. Rate-of-rise heat detectors are unreliable, and prone to false activations (false alarms).

B. Alarms are initiated by rate-of-rise heat detectors at higher temperatures than those required for fixed-temperature devices.

C. Rate-of-rise heat detectors are designed to initiate a signal when the rise in temperature exceeds 12°F to 15°F (7°C to 8°C) in one minute.

D. Rate-of-rise heat detectors are designed to initiate a signal when the rise in temperature exceeds 12°F to 15°F (7°C to 8°C) in ten minutes.

_____ 12. Which of the following statements about rate-compensated heat detectors is MOST accurate? (1189)

A. Rate-compensated heat detectors are designed for areas normally subject to regular temperature changes.

B. Rate-compensated heat detectors use a system of thermistors that produce a change in electrical resistance when exposed to heat.

C. Rate-compensated heat detectors are designed for areas with temperatures far below those found in typical residential occupancies.

D. Rate-compensated heat detectors use a system of pneumatic tubing arranged over the area of coverage to monitor large areas of a building.

_____ 13. Which type of alarm-initiating devices activate in the presence of smoke and other products of combustion? (1190)

A. Pellet detectors

B. Flame detectors

C. Smoke detectors

D. Ultraviolet detectors

_____ 14. Smoke detectors and smoke alarms are activated by: (1190)

A. small amounts of radioactive material in the air.

B. gases released when fire burns in a confined space.

C. the presence of smoke and other products of combustion.

D. flickering light in the ultraviolet and infrared wavelengths.

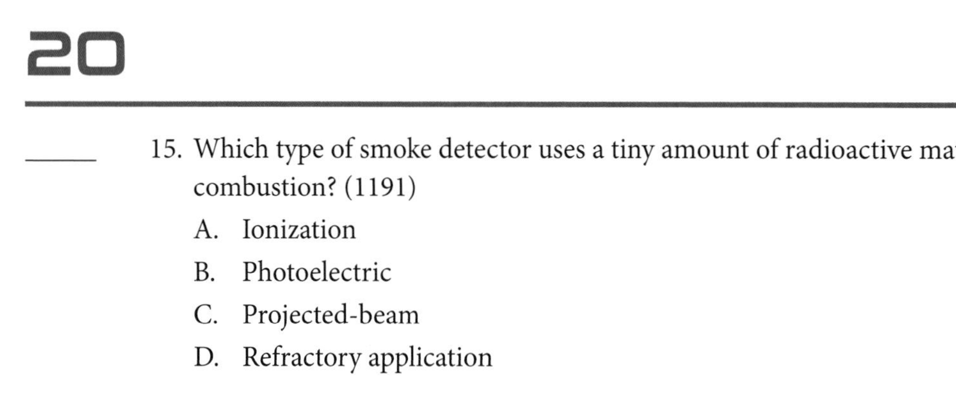

_____ 15. Which type of smoke detector uses a tiny amount of radioactive material to detect products of combustion? (1191)

A. Ionization

B. Photoelectric

C. Projected-beam

D. Refractory application

_____ 16. The basic types of flame detectors are focused on the ____ spectrums. (1193)

A. flicker and infrared

B. ultraviolet and infrared

C. ionization and pneumatic

D. ultraviolet and mercury-vapor

_____ 17. Which of the following statements about sprinkler systems is MOST accurate? (1195)

A. Sprinklers may protrude through the floor on hidden riser pipes.

B. Sprinkler systems are among the least reliable fire protection devices.

C. Sprinkler system components are so simple in design they need not be tested or certified.

D. Sprinkler systems may not perform properly if sprinklers are obstructed by objects stacked too close.

_____ 18. Which of the following statements about sprinkler systems is MOST accurate? (1195)

A. Standards do not discuss requirements for pipe or installation.

B. Sprinkler systems may fail due to objects placed too far from the sprinklers.

C. Most reported sprinkler system failures are generally not due to failure of the actual sprinklers.

D. Sprinkler systems must be designed with the assumption that all sprinklers will activate at one time.

_____ 19. Common sprinkler release mechanisms such as fusible links, frangible bulbs, and chemical pellets open in response to ___. (1197)

A. heat

B. smoke

C. flames

D. fire gases

_____ 20. Temperature ratings of sprinklers can be identified by: (1197)

A. the color-coded chemical pellet.

B. the color-coded sprinkler deflector.

C. the temperature stamped into the sprinkler.

D. the temperature stamped into the frangible bulb.

_____ 21. Which sprinkler orientation type breaks water into a circular pattern of small droplets directed downward? (1198)

A. In-rack

B. Pendant

C. Recessed

D. Concealed

_____ 22. What is the primary purpose of the sprinkler system main control valve? (1200)

A. Simulate the action of one sprinkler

B. Discharge water into sprinkler piping

C. Drain water from the system for maintenance

D. Stop supplying water to the system to save water during droughts

_____ 23. Which sprinkler system operating valve is used to check the system water supply and to allow personnel to drain water from the system for maintenance? (1201)

A. Alarm test valve

B. Main drain valve

C. Main control valve

D. Inspector's test valve

_____ 24. Which of the following statements about the sprinkler system water supply is MOST accurate? (1202)

A. The sprinkler water supply must be obtained from a source separate from the municipal water system.

B. The water supply must be designed to supply enough water at pressure to activate all sprinklers at once.

C. The minimum supply must deliver the required volume of water at the required pressure without the assistance of fire pumps, even in during periods of demand.

D. The minimum supply must deliver the required volume of water to the highest sprinkler in the building at a pressure of 15 psi (105 kPa).

_____ 25. Sprinkler system fire department connections (FDCs) providing additional water pressure should be supplied from pumpers with capacity of at least ___, attached to a minimum of two 2½ inch (65 mm) or larger hoses. (1202-1203)

A. 100 gpm (400 L/min)

B. 1,000 gpm (4 000 L/min)

C. half the municipal water flow

D. the sprinkler system rated flow

_____ 26. Which of the following statements about residential sprinkler systems is MOST accurate? (1208)

A. Residential sprinkler systems are more sensitive than other systems and operate more quickly than other systems.

B. Residential sprinkler systems are designed to extinguish all fires so that occupants do not need to evacuate the structure.

C. Residential sprinkler systems are installed using the same piping and other materials that are used in commercial applications.

D. Residential sprinkler systems are controlled by separate valves, allowing sprinklers to be shut off without affecting domestic water service.

_____ 27. Which of the following statements BEST describes standpipe and hose systems? (1209)

A. NFPA® standards establish four classes of standpipe systems.

B. Standpipe systems allow greater amounts of hose to be deployed during overhaul operations.

C. Design and installation of standpipe systems and hose stations are described in NFPA® 17.

D. Standpipe system components commonly include hose stations, waterflow control valves, pressure-regulating devices, and fire department connections.

_____ 28. Class I standpipe systems are: (1210)

A. also referred to as house lines.

B. primarily used by personnel trained in handling large hoselines.

C. equipped with 1 ½ inch (38 mm) and 2 ½ inch (65 m) hose stations.

D. equipped with a 1 ½ inch (38 mm) hose and nozzle stored on a hose rack system.

_____ 29. Which standpipe classification provides both 1½ inch (38 mm) hose stations to supply water for use by trained building occupants and 2½ inch (65 mm) hose for use by fire departments? (1211)

A. Class I

B. Class II

C. Class III

D. Class IV

_____ 30. Which type of standpipe system has the water supply valve open and pressure maintained in the system at all times, and is capable of meeting system demand automatically? (1211)

A. Manual dry

B. Manual wet

C. Automatic dry

D. Automatic wet

_____ 31. In which smoke control system/method are mechanical fans and ventilation used to create a pressure difference across a barrier, preventing smoke from infiltrating into the high-pressure side? (1214)
A. Exhaust
B. Pressurization
C. Opposed air flow
D. Zoned smoke-control

_____ 32. In which smoke control system/method is the building divided into zones, and mechanical fans used to contain smoke in the zone of fire origin? (1215)
A. Passive
B. Pressurization
C. Opposed air flow
D. Zoned smoke-control

_____ 33. Zoned smoke-control systems are designed to: (1215)
A. introduce fresh air to dilute smoke to acceptable levels for breathing.
B. limit movement of smoke from one compartment of a building to another.
C. use the properties of smoke to collect smoke at the highest point in a large space.
D. use high velocity air aimed at the area of origin to keep smoke from migrating into unaffected areas.

Short Answer

Write the correct answers on the lines provided.

1. List the four main components of a typical alarm system. (1178)

____

____

____

____

2. What are the three basic types of protected premises or local alarm systems? (1182)

____

____

____

3. What are the four basic types of supervising station alarm systems? (1183)

4. List five types of alarm-initiating devices. (1185-1194)

5. What are the two general types of automatic sprinkler systems? (1194)

6. What are three design and installation criteria for sprinkler system installation given in NFPA® 13, 13D and 13R? (1195)

7. List five reasons sprinkler systems may fail. (1195)

8. What are three situations where sprinkler systems alone may not be effective at enhancing life safety? (1195)

9. List five components that are attached to the sprinkler system riser. (1196)

10. According to NFPA® 13, what two things must be contained in a sprinkler storage cabinet? (1198)

11. List five smoke control strategies. (1214)

Firefighter II

Crossword Puzzle

Across

1. System that limits the exposure of building occupants to smoke
3. Alarm system component that transmits a signal when a change occurs
5. System in which alarm signals from the protected premises are transmitted over a leased telephone line or by radio signal to a remote receiving station with a 24-hour staff
6. System component that receives input from automatic and manual fire alarm devices
8. Fire protection system owned and operated by the property owner
9. Detection and alarm device that detects light in the ultraviolet or infrared wave spectrums
12. Alarm system that functions through a constantly attended location (central station) operated by an alarm company
13. Alarm system that alerts and notifies only occupants on the premises of the existence of a fire so that they can safely exit the building and call the fire department
14. System of water pipes, discharge nozzles, and control valves designed to activate during fires by automatically discharging enough water to control or extinguish a fire
15. Alarm-initiating device designed to actuate when visible or invisible products of combustion are present in the room or space where the unit is installed
16. Fire-suppression system that, when activated, expels extinguishing agent from all sprinkler heads in the designated area
17. Electrical device used to indicate the source or location of an activated fire alarm initiating device, may include individual lights located on a schematic map
18. System that connects the protected property with the fire department alarm communications center by a municipal master fire alarm box or over a dedicated telephone line

Down

1. Wet or dry system of pipes with fire hose outlets installed in different areas or on different levels of a building to provide for quick deployment of hoselines during fire fighting operations
2. System designed to protect structure and minimize loss due to fire
4. Temperature-sensitive device that sounds an alarm when the temperature changes at a preset value, such as 12°F to 15°F (7°C to 8°C) per minute
7. Fire-suppression system that consists of closed sprinkler heads attached to a piping system and a secondary detection system; both must operate before the extinguishing agent is released into the system
10. Device used to detect gases produced by a fire within a confined space
11. Part of the sprinkler assembly that creates the discharge pattern of the water

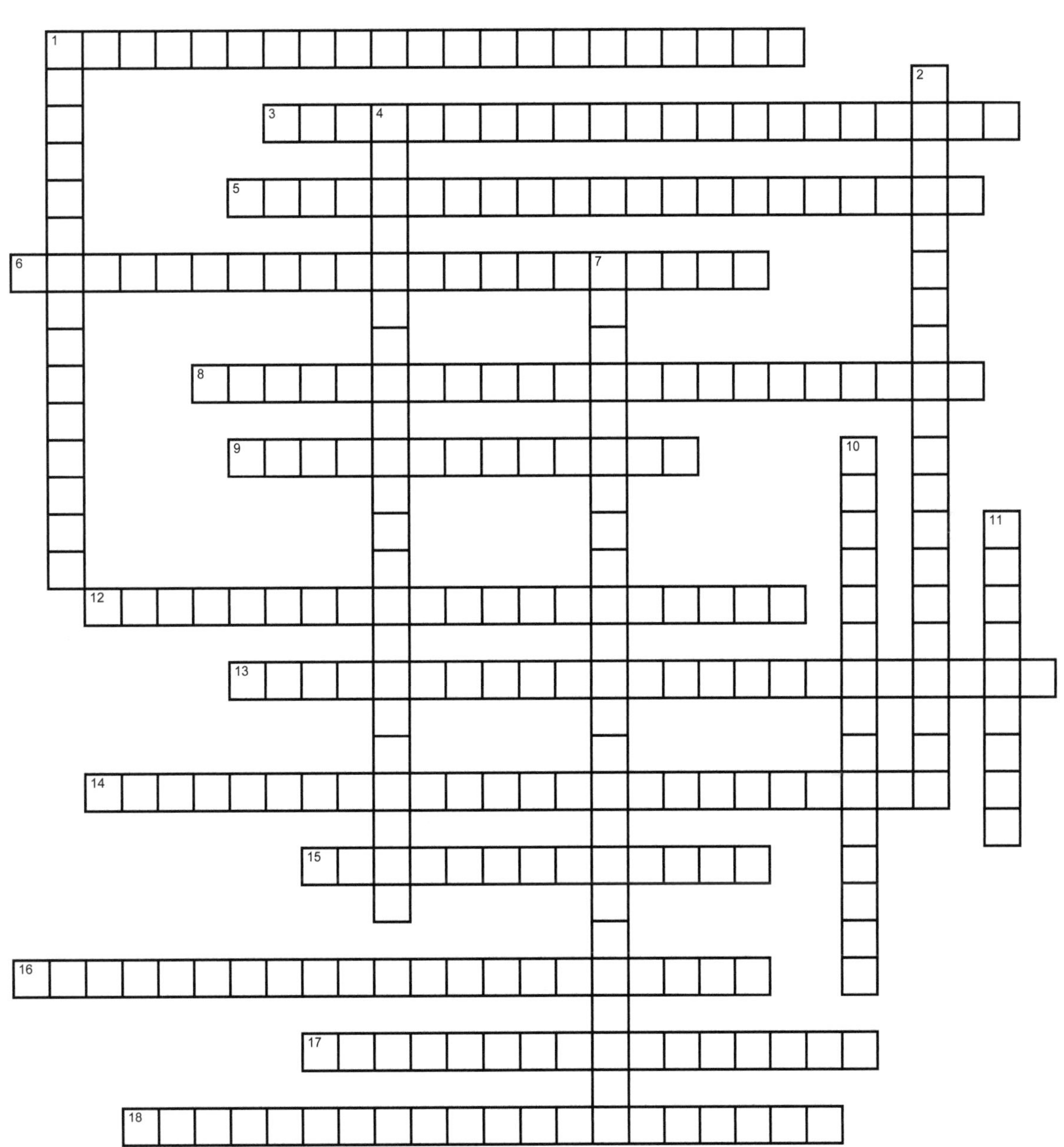
1
2
3
4
5
6
7
8
9
10
11
12
13
14
15
16
17
18

Chapter 21

Fire and Life Safety Initiatives

Firefighter I

Terms

Write the definition of the terms below on the blanks provided.

1. **THIRA (1222)** ____

____

2. **Model Code (1238)** ____

____

True/False

Write True or False on the blanks provided; if False, write the correct statement on the lines provided.

________ 1. To meet responsibilities as part of the life and safety initiatives, a firefighter must understand the value of the program and the development process used to create the program. (1222)

____

____

________ 2. The context of a threat is a brief explanation of the conditions under which a hazard might occur. (1223)

____

____

________ 3. Firefighters delivering public education are only expected to answer questions directly related to fire protection. (1225)

____

____

________ 4. Rapid emergency response to fires is the only responsibility of the fire service. (1226)

____

____

_______ 5. Structure surveys of private residential structures are required by law. (1235)

____

____

_______ 6. Firefighters may learn of a developing juvenile firesetter problem by watching for trends in fires. (1236)

____

____

_______ 7. Codes are enforceable as soon as they are released by the model code organization. (1239)

____

____

_______ 8. The two main aspects of code enforcement are inspection and education. (1239)

____

____

Matching

Write the correct answers on the blanks provided.

Fire and Life Safety Audiences

Match the audience description with the fire and life safety audience. Each choice may be used more than once.

_______ 1. They do not understand cause and effect (1231)

_______ 2. One of the high-risk groups in a community (1234-1235)

_______ 3. Twice as likely to die from fire, leading all other age groups (1234-1235)

_______ 4. What they learn by doing will last longer than what they see or hear (1231)

_______ 5. Appropriate messages include cooking safety and babysitting classes (1232-1233)

_______ 6. Will respond to messages if they believe the information is relevant to them (1233)

_______ 7. Want practical programs they can apply in their personal or professional lives (1233)

_______ 8. Appropriate messages are similar to but more complex than those for preschool (1232)

A. Preschool children
B. Elementary age children
C. Middle school children
D. High school students
E. Adults
F. Older adults

_______ 9. Beginning to take adult responsibilities, but may still have the motivation of children (1232-1233)

_______ 10. Help eliminate any fear of firefighters by having them put equipment on a firefighter (1231)

_______ 11. Appropriate messages include fire service careers, preparation for living independently (1233)

_______ 12. Messages should focus on safe cooking, careless smoking, electrical appliances, and falls (1234-1235)

_______ 13. Programs should involve solving problems, completing tasks, or handling lifestyle choices (1233)

_______ 14. Appropriate messages include survival skills – correct actions to take in event of a natural disaster (1232)

_______ 15. Common messages include home escape plans and fire drills and disaster planning and preparedness (1233)

Multiple Choice

Write the correct answers on the blanks provided.

_____ 1. Hazard identification requires a community to determine the specific hazards it will face, estimate the portion of the population that will be affected, and: (1223)
   A. assess local response capabilities.
   B. determine the threat the hazard will pose.
   C. enact codes and standards to reduce the effects.
   D. determine the educational needs of the affected population.

_____ 2. Identifying hazards to a community requires a review of trends, statistical analysis, and: (1223)
   A. infrastructure.
   B. historical data.
   C. topographic maps.
   D. economic indicators.

_____ 3. Which category of hazard results from an accident or failure of a system or structure? (1223)
   A. Threat
   B. Natural hazard
   C. Technological hazard
   D. Human-caused hazard

_____ 4. Which of the following represents a natural hazard? (1223)
   A. Earthquake
   B. Dam failure
   C. Chemical attack
   D. Threatened biological attack

_____ 5. Which of the following statements about capability assessments is MOST accurate? (1224)

A. Capability assessment results are used to identify threats and hazards.

B. Contingency plans determine if local resources can meet desired outcomes.

C. Capability targets should result in the greatest benefit within the desired time frame.

D. Only direct damage to people and property is considered when determining the effects of a threat.

_____ 6. Which of the following is the BEST example of an enforcement activity assigned to the fire department? (1225)

A. Responding to an emergency involving a structural collapse

B. Investigating the cause of fires and documenting the results

C. Ticketing members of the public who do not wear seat belts

D. Teaching CPR classes to local professional and service organizations

_____ 7. A manufacturer's rebate when a smoke detector is purchased is an example of: (1225)

A. a contingency plan.

B. an economic incentive.

C. a capability assessment.

D. an emergency response.

_____ 8. Which program delivery component provides solutions to prevent a hazard and to reduce harm once the hazard occurs? (1226)

A. Education

B. Engineering

C. Enforcement

D. Emergency response

_____ 9. Fire and life safety education is designed to inform citizens about unsafe behaviors and to: (1226)

A. determine responsibility for intentionally set fires.

B. provide information on how to change those behaviors.

C. issue tickets and fines to citizens engaged in such behaviors.

D. establish minimum requirements for the design, construction, and use of buildings.

_____ 10. Unsafe behaviors or conditions that can result in injury, death, or property damage not related to fire are categorized as: (1226)

A. fire hazards.

B. safety hazards.

C. hazardous processes.

D. high-risk populations.

_____ 11. Hazardous processes may exist temporarily or as a constant function of: (1228)
A. unsafe behaviors.
B. the design of a building.
C. an environmental condition.
D. an industrial or manufacturing site.

_____ 12. Which of the following statements about structural surveys is MOST accurate? (1235)
A. Annual surveys of private residential structures are required by law.
B. Company-level preincident surveys are generally conducted on private residences.
C. Structure surveys are educational opportunities for homeowners and business owners, not for firefighters.
D. Structure surveys are performed by fire departments to become familiar with public access structures and workplaces.

_____ 13. Which of the following groups accounts for 54 percent of all arson arrests? (1236)
A. Males age 18 to 25
B. High-risk older adults
C. All persons age 18 to 25
D. Children under 18 years of age

_____ 14. Which of the following is the BEST message to teach children to prevent development of juvenile firesetters? (1236)
A. The dangers of careless smoking
B. How to safely use fire under adult supervision
C. When clothes are on fire, Stop, Drop, and Roll
D. The reasons that only trained babysitters should be hired

_____ 15. Which of the following messages from a juvenile firesetter program is the MOST appropriate information for adults? (1237)
A. The dangers of careless smoking
B. That matches and lighters are not toys
C. The destructiveness of fire when it is not properly used
D. To supervise young children and never leave them alone with open flames

_____ 16. What steps are taken once a code is adopted? (1239)
A. Model codes are developed and released.
B. Legislative resolution for formal adoption is prepared.
C. Legislative body studies and discusses proposed code.
D. Date is set for implementation and a public announcement is made.

_____ 17. Which of the following BEST describes an activity performed by a fire department inspector? (1239)

A. Assessing local response capabilities
B. Developing a family emergency escape plan
C. Providing data about types and causes of fires in a community
D. Reviewing building plans and conducting construction inspections

_____ 18. Which of the following BEST describes the way a Firefighter I may be involved when working with a fire investigator? (1240)

A. Locate and protect evidence
B. Enforce fire and life safety codes
C. Conduct preincident structure surveys
D. Determine responsibility for intentionally set fires

Short Answer

Write the correct answers on the lines provided.

1. What are three ways a life safety initiatives program is valuable to a fire department and a community? (1222)

____

____

____

____

____

____

2. List the five steps modeled in FEMA's Threat and Hazard Identification and Risk Assessment (THIRA) that communities can follow to develop and implement a fire and life safety initiatives program. (1222)

____

____

____

____

____

3. Threat and Hazard Identification and Risk Assessment (THIRA) threats and hazards are divided into which three broad categories? (1223)

____

____

____

4. List five possible effects a threat or hazard may have on a community. (1224)

____

____

____

____

____

5. What are the "Five Es" of program delivery? (1224)

____

____

____

____

____

6. What are five public education programs related to fire safety and risk reduction that a Firefighter I may be involved with? (1225)

____

____

____

____

____

7. List fifteen unsafe behaviors firefighters should be aware of during preincident planning surveys, home safety surveys, and following emergency incidents. (1227-1228)

8. What are five sources of potential unsafe conditions that will be reduced by proper application of local fire and life safety codes? (1228)

9. Fire and life safety messages can generally be divided into what four categories? (1228)

10. What are the three steps used in a juvenile firesetters program to reduce fires set by children? (1236)

____

____

____

11. List the four categories of juvenile firesetters. (1236)

____

____

____

____

12. What are four steps a firefighter can take to help locate children at risk of becoming juvenile firesetters? (1236)

____

____

____

____

____

____

____

____

13. What are the three model code organizations in North America (one in Canada, two in the United States)? (1238)

____

____

____

True/False

Write True or False on the blanks provided; if False, write the correct statement on the lines provided.

________ 1. Single family private dwellings are not subject to the same requirements of local codes to the same degree as businesses, institutions, and industrial properties. (1240)

________ 2. The main purpose when entering a private residence for a survey is code enforcement. (1243)

________ 3. Safety surveys can alert jurisdictions to local trends in housing development. (1243)

________ 4. The message of each fire and life safety presentation will vary based on the demographics of the intended audience. (1247)

________ 5. Adults with tours should automatically know what to do when an alarm sounds, there is no need to explain that before the tour starts. (1254)

________ 6. All children love station mascots, so be sure to include the animals as a part of the station tour. (1256)

________ 7. Starting a preincident planning survey on the entry floor is the least confusing method to use. (1258)

Fill in the Blank

Write the correct answer on the blanks provided.

1. It is important to use developed resources to ensure that content for fire and life safety messages is valid and accurate. Another way to ensure delivery of accurate messages is that if you do not know the answer to a question, state you ______________________________ and get back to the person. (1249)

2. People remember positives more than negatives. To help avoid confusion about what actions are dangerous, instruct what ________________ rather than emphasizing what ________________. (1249)

3. Seasonal messages and presentations specific to events in the community can allow discussions on important fire and life safety messages. This type of message is called a ________________ message and is based on a variety of factors. (1250)

Identification

Identify the following items on the lines provided. (1259)
Courtesy of Sanborn Map Company

1. ______________________________

H

4. ______________________________

20" W.P. (H.P.F.S.)

2. ______________________________

5. ______________________________

E

3. ______________________________

6" W.P.
4" W.P.

6. ______________________________

6" W.P. (PRIV.)

7. ______________________________

10. ______________________________

NS

3

8. ______________________________

11. ______________________________

STAIRS

D.H.

9. ______________________________

12. ______________________________

Matching

Write the correct answers on the blanks provided.

Vocal Characteristics

Match the vocal characteristic with the description. Each choice will be used once.

_______ 1. Vary the pitch of words, syllables, or phrases to emphasize important points (1246)

_______ 2. Clearly emphasize each syllable and accent; avoid slurring (1246)

_______ 3. Use the correct tense, possession, and pronoun agreement (1246)

_______ 4. Speak loudly and clearly enough to be heard at the back of the room (1246)

_______ 5. Say each word correctly, stressing the right syllables, and pausing where appropriate (1246)

_______ 6. Use changes in loudness, tone, and rate (1246)

A. Pronunciation
B. Good grammar
C. Inflection
D. Variety
E. Enunciation
F. Projection

Organization of the Message

Match the organization type with the description of the method. Each choice will only be used once.

_____ 1. Begins with basic and moves to more difficult knowledge as the presentation progresses (1251)

_____ 2. Begins by teaching each step, then asks audience members to practice in that order (1251)

_____ 3. Begins with information audience knows before moving to unfamiliar information (1251)

_____ 4. Begins with an overview, breaks the message into parts, closes with a summary (1251)

A. Known-to-unknown

B. Simple-to-complex

C. Whole-part-whole

D. Step-by-step

Multiple Choice

Write the correct answers on the blanks provided.

_____ 1. Which of the following BEST describes a common cause of residential fires that firefighters should look for during private residential surveys? (1241)

A. Exposed electrical wiring
B. Extension cords used correctly
C. Well maintained electrical appliances
D. Appropriate placement of combustibles

_____ 2. What educational opportunities can firefighters take advantage of after identifying hazards in aprivate residential survey? (1243)

A. Reschedule for next inspection
B. Critique exit plan and note flaws
C. Explain fines from code violations
D. Discuss advantages of residential sprinkler systems

_____ 3. Which BEST describes how private residential surveys should be performed? (1244)

A. By one firefighter on a surprise survey basis, focused on basements
B. By one firefighter, mailing results after comparing to local codes to find violations
C. In teams of two or more, complimenting occupants when favorable conditions are found
D. In teams of three, opening any closed doors as the survey proceeds without asking permission

_____ 4. If hazardous conditions are found during a private residential survey, a firefighter should: (1244)
A. contact local code enforcement agencies to initiate fine process.
B. require that all areas of the structure be reinspected in two weeks.
C. offer constructive suggestions for correcting or eliminating the conditions.
D. leave immediately, requesting residents contact station again when conditions are corrected.

_____ 5. When presenting to young children, what type of group setting is the best? (1252)
A. Small groups
B. Combining at least two classroom groups
C. Large presentations in the gym or auditorium
D. Groups of at least twenty students and no other adults

_____ 6. Which of the following BEST describes children's common fears? (1252)
A. Loud noises
B. Large groups
C. Repeating words
D. Practicing safety steps

_____ 7. Which of the following BEST describes the learning style of young children? (1253)
A. They learn best using all five senses.
B. One time is enough for them to learn the message.
C. By constantly repeating words, children learn a message.
D. Messages can simply be told, they do not need to be illustrated.

_____ 8. Which of the following may need to be prepared for station visitors prior to station tours? (1254)
A. A system for climbing on apparatus
B. A method to participate in cleaning PPE
C. A place to leave coats and personal effects
D. A place to interact with station mascots unattended

_____ 9. What can the documentation in preincident planning surveys be used for? (1256)
A. To enhance the department's public image
B. To present seasonally appropriate messages to the public
C. To identify code violations that fines should be assessed for
D. To visualize how standard tactics may not apply in various occupancies

_____ 10. What can the documentation in preincident planning surveys be used for? (1256)
A. To check for emergency telephone number stickers
B. To leave behind educational materials appropriate for occupants
C. To determine if there are occupants with language barriers that may require translators
D. To notify that a safety survey has been conducted by leaving behind a department card

_____ 11. Which of the following BEST describes what to note during a preincident planning survey? (1257)
A. The grouping methods used during presentations
B. The demographic groups represented by occupants of the building
C. The types of apparatus, fire attack tactics, and other strategies used at previous incidents
D. The location of fire hydrants, fire department connections, water control valves, and water supply sources

_____ 12. Photos taken during a preincident planning survey should be taken from what position when possible? (1260)
A. Any position that is allowed by building occupants
B. An elevated position, from an adjoining building if needed
C. Whatever position is easiest to take from the building interior
D. A position that allows a direct view in ground floor windows

Short Answer

Write the correct answers on the lines provided.

1. What are five of the basic presentation skills that should be used when making fire and life safety presentations? (1246-1247)

____
____
____
____
____
____
____
____

2. What can preincident planning surveys assist with? (1256)

Chapter 22

Emergency Medical Care for Fire Department First Responders

Terms

Write the definition of the terms below on the blanks provided.

1. **Emergency Medical Services (EMS) (1272)**____________________

2. **Cross-Training (1272)** ____________________

3. **Emergency Medical Technician (EMT) (1272)** ____________________

4. **Paramedic (1272)** ____________________

5. **Protected Medical Information (PMI) (1272)** ____________________

6. **Communicable Diseases (1273)**____________________

7. **Body Substance Isolation (BSI) (1273)** ____________________

8. **Immunization (1277)** ____________________

9. **Pathogens (1277)** ____________________

10. **Airway (1281)** ______________________________

____

11. **Pulse (1282)** ______________________________

____

12. **Cardiac Arrest (1282)** ______________________________

____

13. **Clinical Death (1282)** ______________________________

____

14. **Biological Death (1282)** ______________________________

____

15. **Defibrillation (1283)** ______________________________

____

16. **Automated External Defibrillator (AED) (1283)** ______________________________

____

17. **Cardiopulmonary Resuscitation (CPR) (1284)** ______________________________

____

18. **Chest Compression (1284)** ______________________________

____

19. **Rigor Mortis (1284)** ______________________________

____

20. **Line of Lividity (1284)** ______________________________

____

21. **Artery (1289)** ____

____

22. **Vein (1289)** ____

____

23. **Capillaries (1289)** ____

____

24. **Dressing (1290)** ____

____

25. **Shock (1292)** ____

____

26. **Hypovolemic Shock (1292)** ____

____

27. **Cardiogenic Shock (1292)** ____

____

28. **Neurogenic Shock (1292)** ____

____

29. **Anaphylactic Shock (1293)** ____

____

30. **Septic Shock (1293)** ____

____

True/False

Write True or False on the blanks provided; if False, write the correct statement on the lines provided.

_______ 1. Fire departments often respond as medical first responders and begin care until EMS personnel arrive. (1272)

____

____

_______ 2. Tuberculosis exposure is determined by injecting an inactive bacterium under the skin. (1277)

____

____

_______ 3. Airborne pathogens are the most commonly encountered pathogens. (1277)

____

____

_______ 4. Sealed containers for the disposal of gloves soiled with blood and other body fluids are typically green in color. (1279)

____

____

_______ 5. Helmet shields provide suitable eye protection for emergency medical use. (1279)

____

____

_______ 6. Medical equipment and non-disposable PPE that comes into contact with any patient must be considered contaminated. (1280)

____

____

_______ 7. Sharps, including needles and blades, can be disposed of in the regular trash if wrapped in old newspapers. (1280)

____

____

_______ 8. If no pulse is found in an unresponsive patient, immediately begin a cycle of chest compressions. (1281)

____

____

_______ 9. If the patient is able to talk and appears to be breathing without difficulty, it can be assumed that the airway is clear. (1281)

____

____

_______ 10. It typically takes stronger blood flow for the pulse to be felt in the carotid artery. (1282)

____

____

_______ 11. When performing CPR it is normal for some type of cracking of sternum or ribs to be heard or felt during compressions. (1286)

____

____

_______ 12. Direct pressure is the first and most commonly used method to control bleeding. (1290)

____

____

Matching

Write the correct answers on the blanks provided.

Communicable Diseases

Match the description with the communicable disease listed. Each choice will be used once.

_________ 1. Spread through contact with infected blood and body fluids; weakens immune system to the point where the body is unable to fight off diseases (1276)

_________ 2. An increasing concern in healthcare settings, difficult to control; does not typically respond to normal antibiotic treatment (1276)

_________ 3. Bacterial infection that primarily affects the respiratory system (1275)

_________ 4. Virus that has more than likely done serious liver damage even while individual is symptom free (1275)

_________ 5. Generally short-term; with symptoms including fatigue, abdominal pain, and marked yellowing of the skin and/or eyes (1274)

A. HIV/Aids
B. Hepatitis A
C. Hepatitis C
D. Tuberculosis
E. Multi Drug-Resistant Organisms

Types of Shock

Match the cause with the type of shock listed. Each choice will be used once.

_________ 1. Caused by loss of blood (1292)

_________ 2. Caused by poor cardiac output (1292)

_________ 3. Caused by overexpansion of blood vessels due to damage to the brain, spinal cord, or other nerves (1292)

_________ 4. Caused by severe allergic reactions (1293)

_________ 5. Caused by severe infection in the body (1293)

A. Septic
B. Cardiogenic
C. Neurogenic
D. Anaphylactic
E. Hypovolemic

Multiple Choice

Write the correct answers on the blanks provided.

_____ 1. Which of the following dictates how and to whom protected medical information (PMI) can be shared? (1272)

A. Federal Health Information Act
B. Patient Requirements Medical Act
C. Access and Use Medical Information Act
D. Health Insurance Portability and Accountability Act

_____ 2. Which type of viral hepatitis is often contracted by exposure to contaminated fecal matter? (1274)

A. Hepatitis A

B. Hepatitis B

C. Hepatitis C

D. Hepatitis D

_____ 3. Which type of viral hepatitis is rare and only occurs when the patient is also infected by Hepatitis B? (1275)

A. Hepatitis A

B. Hepatitis B-2

C. Hepatitis C

D. Hepatitis D

_____ 4. For which communicable disease should a first responder follow body substance isolation practices and wear an N-95 mask? (1276)

A. MRSA

B. HIV/Aids

C. Hepatitis

D. Tuberculosis

_____ 5. When following proper body substance isolation (BSI) practices, hands should be washed for: (1278)

A. no less than 15 seconds.

B. no less than 30 seconds.

C. no less than 60 seconds.

D. no less than 90 seconds.

_____ 6. When determining patient assessment for a victim that is responsive, the first assessment should be: (1280)

A. airway.

B. breathing.

C. circulation.

D. blood loss.

_____ 7. The second assessment performed for a responsive victim should be: (1280)

A. airway.

B. breathing.

C. circulation.

D. blood loss.

_____ 8. When working with a responsive victim, responders will assess ___ as the third assessment. (1282)

A. airway
B. breathing
C. circulation
D. blood loss

_____ 9. When determining patient assessment for a victim that is unresponsive, the first assessment should be: (1281)

A. airway.
B. breathing.
C. circulation.
D. blood loss.

_____ 10. When working with an unresponsive victim, responders will assess ___ as the second assessment. (1281)

A. airway
B. breathing
C. circulation
D. blood loss

_____ 11. Which assessment is made by listening to the patient's mouth or nose? (1282)

A. Airway
B. Breathing
C. Circulation
D. Blood loss

_____ 12. When performing CPR on adults, chest compressions should be administered by quickly and firmly depressing the chest at a rate of at least: (1285)

A. 50 compressions per minute.
B. 100 compressions per minute.
C. 150 compressions per minute.
D. 200 compressions per minute.

_____ 13. When performing CPR, rescuers should use only one hand with: (1286)

A. children.
B. small adults.
C. older victims.
D. victims with blood loss.

_____ 14. When performing CPR on children, chest compressions should be administered by quickly and firmly depressing the chest at a rate of at least: (1286)

A. 50 compressions per minute.

B. 100 compressions per minute.

C. 150 compressions per minute.

D. 200 compressions per minute.

_____ 15. When performing CPR on infants, chest compressions should be administered by quickly and firmly depressing the chest at a rate of at least: (1287)

A. 25 compressions per minute.

B. 50 compressions per minute.

C. 100 compressions per minute.

D. 150 compressions per minute.

_____ 16. Which type of external bleeding may require surgical intervention in order for it to stop? (1289)

A. Venous

B. Arterial

C. Capillary

D. Orifice

_____ 17. Which type of external bleeding is darker in color because oxygen has been removed by cells and carbon dioxide and waste have been added? (1289)

A. Venous

B. Arterial

C. Capillary

D. Orifice

_____ 18. Which type of external bleeding tends to ooze from injuries and is often of limited quantity? (1290)

A. Venous

B. Arterial

C. Capillary

D. Orifice

_____ 19. Which of the following is a sign of decompensated shock? (1293)

A. Hot, dry skin

B. Nose bleeds

C. Nausea and/or vomiting

D. Being intermittently hot and cold

_____ 20. Patients who exhibit signs and symptoms of shock should: (1293)

A. be re-evaluated every five minutes.
B. wait for advanced treatment on scene.
C. be immediately transported to a hospital.
D. not be moved from the scene until stabilized.

Short Answer

Write the correct answers on the blanks provided.

1. What are the three ways that ambulance services are provided? (1272)

____
____
____
____
____
____

2. What information is considered protected medical information (PMI)? (1272)

____
____
____

3. What immunizations may be required or recommended for first responders? (1277)

____
____
____
____
____

4. What procedures are included in body substance isolation (BSI)? (1277-1280)

____
____
____

5. What will an automated external defibrillator (AED) do when used by a layperson? (1283)

6. If CPR has been initiated, under what conditions should it be discontinued? (1288)

7. What are three signs of internal bleeding? (1291)

Crossword Puzzle

Across

1. Disease that is transmissible from one person to another
5. Professional level of certification for emergency medical personnel who are trained in advanced life support procedures
11. A colored area of the corpse that is noticeably contrasted from the rest of the body caused by the pooling of blood
13. Information of a patient that includes personal data (name, birth date, social security number, address), medical history, and condition
14. Condition present when irreversible brain damage has occurred, usually 4 to 10 minutes after cardiac arrest
17. Shock caused by a severe infection in the body
19. Organisms that cause infection, such as viruses and bacteria

Down

2. The practice of taking proactive, protective measures to isolate body substances in order to prevent the spread of infectious disease
3. The delivery of a measured dose of electrical current by a special machine in order to regain normal function of the heart
4. Shock caused by the overexpansion of blood vessels due to damage to the brain, spinal cord, or other nerves
6. Shock caused by a severe allergic reaction
7. Training emergency services personnel to function in more than one capacity
8. Term that refers to the lack of signs of life, where there is no pulse and no blood pressure; occurs immediately after the onset of cardiac arrest
9. Shock caused by poor cardiac output
10. Cardiac defibrillator designed for layperson use that analyzes the cardiac rhythm and determines if defibrillation is warranted
12. Shock caused by loss of blood
15. Application of rescue breathing and external cardiac compression used on patients in cardiac arrest to provide an adequate circulation and oxygen to support life
16. Professional-level provider of basic life support emergency medical care
18. Initial medical evaluation/treatment provided to employees and others who become ill or are injured

1
2
3
4
5
6
7
8
9
10
11
12
13
14
15
16
17
18
19

Chapter 23

Hazards, Behavior, and Identification of Hazardous Materials/WMD

Terms

Write the definition of the terms below on the blanks provided.

1. **Hazardous Material (1300)** ____

____

2. **Dangerous Goods (1300)** ____

____

3. **Weapon of Mass Destruction (1300)** ____

____

4. **Terrorism (1300)** ____

____

5. **Hazard (1300)** ____

____

6. **Acute Health Effects (1301)** ____

____

7. **Chronic Health Effects (1301)** ____

____

8. **Polymerization (1302)** ____

____

9. **Elevated-Temperature Material (1302)** ____

____

10. **Cryogens (1302)** ______________________________

____

11. **Poison (1302)** ______________________________

____

12. **Ionizing Radiation (1302)** ______________________________

____

13. **Nonionizing Radiation (1303)** ______________________________

____

14. **Protons (1303)** ______________________________

____

15. **Electron (1303)** ______________________________

____

16. **Photon (1303)** ______________________________

____

17. **Exposure (1304)** ______________________________

____

18. **Routes of Entry (1304)** ______________________________

____

19. **Radiation Dose (1305)** ______________________________

____

20. **Corrosive Material (1306)** ______________________________

____

21. **Systemic Effect (1306)** ____

____

22. **Ion (1308)** ____

____

23. **Etiological Hazards (1309)** ____

____

24. **Infectious (1310)** ____

____

25. **Contagious (1310)** ____

____

26. **Improvised Explosive Device (IED) (1311)** ____

____

27. **Reactivity (1311)** ____

____

28. **Boiling Point (1315)** ____

____

29. **Water Solubility (1316)** ____

____

30. **Persistence (1316)** ____

____

31. **Dispersion (1316)** ____

____

32. **Activation Energy (1318)** ______________________________

____

33. **Strong Oxidizer (1318)** ______________________________

____

34. **Catalyst (1320)** ______________________________

____

35. **Inhibitor (1320)** ______________________________

____

36. **Carboy (1330)** ______________________________

____

37. **Emergency Response Guidebook (*ERG*) (1365)** ______________________________

____

38. **Reporting Marks (1365)** ______________________________

____

39. **Capacity Stencil (1367)** ______________________________

____

40. **Specification Marking (1367)** ______________________________

____

41. **Safety Data Sheet (SDS) (1370)** ______________________________

____

42. **Signal Word (1371)** ______________________________

____

43. **Bill of Lading (1376)** ______________________________

____

44. **Olfactory Fatigue (1382)** ______________________________

____

45. **Illicit Clandestine Laboratory (1383)** ______________________________

____

46. **Toxic Industrial Material (TIM) (1383)** ______________________________

____

47. **Chemical Warfare Agent (1385)** ______________________________

____

48. **Radiological Dispersal Device (RDD) (1389)** ______________________________

____

49. **Electromagnetic Pulse (EMP) (1389)** ______________________________

____

50. **Meth Lab (1390)** ______________________________

____

51. **Phosphine (1392)** ______________________________

____

52. **Choking Agent (1392)** ______________________________

____

53. **Organophosphate Pesticides (1397)** ______________________________

____

54. **Sarin (GB) (1397)** ______________________________

____

55. **Glove Box (1402)** ______________________________

____

56. **Autoclave (1402)** ______________________________

____

57. **Nebulizer (1402)** ______________________________

____

58. **Secondary Device (1402)** ______________________________

____

True/False

Write True or False on the blanks provided; if False, write the correct statement on the lines provided.

_______ 1. A hazardous material is a weapon or device that can cause death or serious injury to a large number of people. (1300)

____

____

_______ 2. Acute health effects are short-term conditions that appear within hours or days. (1301)

____

____

_______ 3. Simple asphyxiants prohibit the body from processing available oxygen. (1305)

____

____

_______ 4. Convulsants cause involuntary muscle contraction. (1309)

____

____

_______ 5. A paint supply store is highly likely to house hazardous materials. (1327)

____

____

_______ 6. Ton containers typically contain anhydrous ammonia. (1339)

_______ 7. UN identification numbers are provided in the green-bordered section of the *ERG*. (1365)

_______ 8. The NFPA® 704 system displays the instability hazard on a blue background. (1369-1370)

_______ 9. Pesticides that have moderate toxicity should be labeled with WARNING. (1373)

_______ 10. Safety data sheets must accompany shipments of hazardous materials. (1376)

_______ 11. Hearing is the safest of the senses to use in detecting the presence of hazardous materials. (1380)

_______ 12. Nausea and vomiting may indicate the presence of hazardous materials. (1382)

_______ 13. Monitoring and detection devices require specialized training. (1383)

_______ 14. Secondary devices may be used during terrorist attacks or criminal events. (1402)

_______ 15. To avoid booby traps, responders should be careful when touching or moving loose items. (1405)

____

____

Identification

Identify the following items on the lines provided.

Railroad Cars (1335-1338)

1. ____

2. ____

3. ________________________________

4. ________________________________

5. ________________________________

6. ________________________________

23

Cargo Tank Trucks (1340-1344)

1. ______________________________

4. ______________________________

2. ______________________________

5. ______________________________

3. ______________________________

6. ______________________________

7. ____

Matching

Write the correct answers on the blanks provided.

Types of Hazards

Match the description with the type of hazard listed. Each choice will be used once.

________	1. Hazards that involve extreme heat or cold (1302)	A. Asphyxiation
________	2. Most common at medical centers, nuclear power plants, research facilities, and transportation incidents (1302)	B. Etiological or Biological
________	3. Hazards that prevent the body from absorbing oxygen (1305)	C. Mechanical
________	4. Microorganisms that cause severe illness or disease (1309)	D. Radiological
________	5. Hazards that cause injury through blunt physical force (1311)	E. Thermal

23

Physical Properties

Match the description with the type of property listed. Each choice will be used once.

_________ 1. Measure of a substance's tendency to evaporate (1314)

_________ 2. Temperature at which vapor pressure is equal to or greater than atmospheric pressure (1315)

_________ 3. The weight of pure vapor or gas compared to the weight of an equal volume of dry air, at the same temperature and pressure (1315)

_________ 4. Percentage of a material that dissolves in water at ambient temperature (1316)

_________ 5. Density of a substance compared to density of some standard material (1316)

_________ 6. Ability to remain in the environment (1316)

_________ 7. Ability of a substance to chemically react with other materials (1318)

A. Boiling Point
B. Persistence
C. Reactivity
D. Solubility
E. Specific Gravity
F. Vapor Density
G. Vapor Pressure

Indicators of a Terrorist Attack

Match the description with the indicator listed. Each choice can be used more than once.

_________ 1. Casualties distributed downwind or near ventilation systems (1385)

_________ 2. Diseases that do not normally occur in the geographic area (1388)

_________ 3. Electromagnetic pulse (1389)

_________ 4. Glowing material (1309)

_________ 5. Large numbers of people with flu-like symptoms outside of flu season (1389)

_________ 6. Material that is hot without any sign of an external heat source (1389)

_________ 7. Multiple fires or explosions (1390)

_________ 8. Mushroom cloud (1389)

_________ 9. Propane or other flammable gas cylinders in unusual locations (1390)

_________ 10. Suspicious packages that weigh more than they should (1389)

_________ 11. Unattended packages/backpacks/objects left in public areas (1390)

_________ 12. Unexplained odors or tastes that seem inappropriate for the location (1385)

_________ 13. Unexplained patterns of sudden, similar, nontraumatic illnesses or death (1387)

_________ 14. Unusual spraying activity (1388)

A. Biological attack indicators
B. Chemical attack indicators
C. Explosive/incendiary attack indicators
D. Nuclear attack indicators
E. Radiological attack indicators

Multiple Choice

Write the correct answers on the blanks provided.

_____ 1. What is the U.S. or Canadian term for hazardous materials aboard an aircraft? (1300)
   A. Hazardous goods
   B. Dangerous goods
   C. Dangerous materials
   D. Weapons of mass destruction

_____ 2. What type of ionizing radiation loses energy rapidly when traveling through matter? (1303)
   A. Beta
   B. Alpha
   C. Gamma
   D. Neutron

_____ 3. What type of ionizing radiation can be stopped by two inches (50 mm) of lead or several feet (m) of earth? (1303)
   A. Beta
   B. Alpha
   C. Gamma
   D. Neutron

_____ 4. Which types of chemical hazards are chemicals that cause permanent damage to anything they touch? (1308)
   A. Poisons
   B. Irritants
   C. Corrosives
   D. Carcinogens

_____ 5. Which types of biological hazards are produced by living organisms? (1310)
   A. Viruses
   B. Bacteria
   C. Rickettsias
   D. Biological toxins

_____ 6. Which type of mechanical hazard occurs when blasts near ground level create shock waves? (1312)
   A. Seismic effect
   B. Shock wave effect
   C. Blast-pressure waves
   D. Shrapnel fragmentation

_____ 7. Which types of hazardous materials are present in air and create a potential inhalation hazard? (1313)

A. Solid hazardous materials
B. Liquid hazardous materials
C. Gaseous hazardous materials
D. Vaporous hazardous materials

_____ 8. Which of the following are examples of bulk transportation containers? (1339)

A. Reactors
B. Pipelines
C. Intermodal containers
D. Aboveground storage tanks

_____ 9. Intermediate bulk containers have a maximum capacity of not more than: (1339)

A. 3 m^3 (3 000 L; 793 gal; 106 ft^3).
B. 6 m^3 (6 000 L; 1 585 gal; 212 ft^3).
C. 9 m^3 (9 000 L; 2 377 gal; 318 ft^3).
D. 12 m^3 (12 000 L; 3 170 gal; 424 ft^3).

_____ 10. UN identification numbers must be displayed on: (1355)

A. portable tanks.
B. all nonbulk packages.
C. certain bulk packages.
D. military transport containers.

_____ 11. Which North American railroad tank car markings may be used to get information about the car's contents and construction from the railroad or shipper? (1365)

A. Reporting marks
B. Capacity stencils
C. Specification markings
D. Identification markings

_____ 12. The NFPA® 704 system is NOT designed for: (1369)

A. biological agents.
B. chemical hazards.
C. underground storage tanks.
D. above ground storage tanks.

_____ 13. Manufacturer labels are required on all: (1371)

A. hazardous products in Canada.
B. hazardous products in the U.S.
C. chemical product containers in Canada.
D. chemical product containers in the U.S.

_____ 14. On trucks, shipping papers are typically found: (1377)

A. near the driver.
B. in the trailer of the truck.
C. with the shipping company.
D. with the Department of Transportation (DOT).

_____ 15. Which of the following statements regarding the *ERG* is MOST accurate? (1379)

A. The ERG should be used in conjunction with other resources.
B. The ERG is primarily designed for use at fixed-facility locations.
C. The ERG addresses all possible circumstances associated with dangerous goods/hazardous materials incidents.
D. The ERG is designed for bystanders who may be the first to arrive at the scene of a dangerous goods/hazardous materials incident.

_____ 16. How do terrorist attacks differ from other hazardous materials incidents? (1384)

A. They deliberately target people.
B. They typically require less manpower.
C. They have a lesser risk from structural collapse.
D. They rarely involve booby traps or secondary devices.

_____ 17. Which of the following is an indicator of a methamphetamine lab? (1397)

A. Glove boxes or biological safety cabinets
B. Alterations to building ventilation systems
C. Discoloration of structures, pavement, and soil
D. Chemicals such as methyl iodide and phosphorous trichloride

_____ 18. Which of the following target responders who are already at the scene of an incident? (1402)

A. Chemical toxins
B. Primary devices
C. Secondary devices
D. Explosive ordnance

Short Answer

Write the correct answers on the blanks provided.

1. What are the four routes of entry for hazardous materials? (1312)

2. List in order the six stages of the General Emergency Behavior Model (GEBMO). (1320-1325)

3. In what ways does terrorism intend to do harm? (1328-1329)

4. What are the indications of a physical action? (1381)

5. What are four indications of a chemical reaction? (1381)

____

____

____

____

6. List five pieces of equipment used to make methamphetamine. (1392)

____

____

____

____

____

7. What are five indicators of an explosive lab? (1400-1401)

____

____

____

____

8. What are three guidelines for protecting against possible secondary devices? (1403)

____

____

____

23

Crossword Puzzle

Across

1. Chemicals that kill insects by disrupting their central nervous systems; because they have the same effect on humans, they are sometimes used in terrorist attacks
4. Ability of a liquid or solid to mix with or dissolve in water
10. Health effects that develop rapidly
12. Means by which hazardous materials enter the body; inhalation, ingestion, skin contact, injection, absorption, and penetration
13. Harmful viruses and bacteria; when used deliberately, they are also known as Biological Weapons
14. Bomb or other weapon that targets responders and bystanders who are already at the scene of an incident
15. Ability of a substance to chemically react with other materials, and the speed with which that reaction takes place
16. Length of time a chemical agent remains effective without dissipating
17. Radiation that causes a chemical change in atoms by removing their electrons

Down

2. Substance that can be dangerous to human health or the environment if not properly controlled
3. Stencil on the exterior of a tank car indicating the standards to which the tank car was built
4. Weapon or device that can cause death or serious injury to a large number of people
5. Manual that identifies hazardous materials labels/placards; also outlines initial actions to be taken at haz mat incidents
6. Homemade bomb that is not deployed in a conventional military fashion
7. Number stenciled on the exterior of a tank car to indicate the volume of the tank
8. Combination of letters and numbers stenciled on rail tank cars that may be used to get information about the car's contents from the railroad or the shipper
9. Long-term health effects, often resulting from exposure to a hazardous substance
11. Process of being spread widely

1
2
3
4
5
6
7
8
9
10
11
12
13
14
15
16
17

Chapter 24

Mitigating Haz Mat/WMD Incidents

Terms

Write the definition of the terms below on the blanks provided.

1. **Occupational Safety and Health Administration (OSHA) (1413)** ____________________

2. **Environmental Protection Agency (EPA) (1413)** ____________________

3. **Hazardous Waste Operations and Emergency Response (HAZWOPER) (1413)** ____________________

4. **Awareness-Level (1414)** ____________________

5. **Operations-Level (1414)** ____________________

6. **Dam/Dike (1416)** ____________________

7. **Divert (1416)** ____________________

8. **Unified Command (1418)** ____________________

9. **Incident Action Plan (IAP) (1419)** ____________________

10. **National Response Framework (NRF) (1420)**

11. **Hazard and Risk Assessment (1424)**

12. **Plug (1425)**

13. **Defensive Strategy (1428)**

14. **Offensive Strategy (1428)**

15. **Nonintervention Strategy (1428)**

16. **Confinement (1430)**

17. **Containment (1430)**

18. **Toxic Inhalation Hazard (TIH) (1432)**

19. **Initial Isolation Distance (1434)**

20. **Initial Isolation Zone (1434)**

21. **Street Clothes (1435)** ____

____

22. **Chemical-Protective Clothing (CPC) (1435)** ____

____

23. **Evacuation (1435)** ____

____

24. **Decontamination (1437)** ____

____

25. **Cross Contamination (1437)** ____

____

26. **Protective Action Distance (1437)** ____

____

27. **Emergency Breathing Support System (EBSS) (1444)** ____

____

28. **Permeation (1449)** ____

____

29. **Breakthrough Time (1452)** ____

____

30. **Liquid-Splash Protective Clothing (1453)** ____

____

31. **Vapor-Protective Clothing (1453)** ____

____

32. **Encapsulating (1453)** ____________________

33. **Level A Protection (1455)**____________________

34. **Level B Protection (1455)**____________________

35. **Level C Protection (1458)**____________________

36. **Level D Protection (1459)** ____________________

37. **Heat Stress (1461)**____________________

38. **Heat Stroke (1461)** ____________________

39. **Heat Exhaustion (1461)** ____________________

40. **Heat Cramps (1461)** ____________________

41. **Heat Rash (1461)** ____________________

42. **Frostbite (1463)** ____________________

43. **Trench Foot (1463)** ______________________________

____

44. **Hot Zone (1468)** ______________________________

____

45. **Warm Zone (1468)** ______________________________

____

46. **Cold Zone (1470)** ______________________________

____

47. **Staging Area (1470)** ______________________________

____

48. **Transportation Area (1470)** ______________________________

____

49. **Mutual Aid (1471)** ______________________________

____

50. **Automatic Aid (1471)** ______________________________

____

51. **Inverse Square Law (1475)** ______________________________

____

52. **Self-Presenters (1480)** ______________________________

____

53. **Emergency Decontamination (1482)** ______________________________

____

54. **Triage (1485)** ______________________________

____

55. **Turbulence (1492)** ______________________________

____

True/False

Write True or False on the blanks provided; if False, write the correct statement on the lines provided.

_______ 1. Awareness-Level personnel are expected to recognize the type of container at a site and identify the material in it if possible. (1414)

____

____

_______ 2. NIMS-ICS is designed to be applicable to only complex, large-scale incidents. (1419)

____

____

_______ 3. A Level I incident is the most serious type of incident. (1424)

____

____

_______ 4. Strategic goals are broad statements of what must be done to resolve the incident. (1427)

____

____

_______ 5. Implementing the incident action plan is performed after strategic goals have been selected. (1430)

____

____

_______ 6. The *ERG* addresses all possible circumstances that may be associated with a dangerous goods/hazardous materials incident. (1431)

____

____

_______ 7. The *ERG* Table of Initial Isolation and Protective Action Distances is divided into daytime and nighttime situations. (1440)

_______ 8. Use of SCBA can create limited vision and communications. (1454)

_______ 9. EPA Level C ensembles are used only for nuisance contamination with no atmospheric hazards. (1458)

_______ 10. PPE inspection, testing, and maintenance must be in accordance with manufacturer's recommendations. (1465)

_______ 11. Notification requirements are spelled out in NIMS-ICS. (1471)

_______ 12. Technical decon may be used on victims in non-life-threatening situations. (1485)

_______ 13. Rescue is a difficult strategy to implement, particularly in the initial stages. (1485)

_______ 14. A critique compiles information obtained from debriefings and postincident reports. (1498)

24

Matching

Write the correct answers on the blanks provided.

ICS Haz Mat Positions

Match the ICS Haz Mat position listed with the correct description. Each choice will be used once.

_____ 1. Manages the resources assigned to the branch or group (1416)

_____ 2. Supervises all companies and personnel operating in the hazardous area (1416)

_____ 3. Supervises operations in the scene control zone where decontamination is conducted (1416)

_____ 4. Controls all movement of personnel and equipment between the control zones (1417)

_____ 5. Responsible for the overall safety of assigned personnel within the Hazardous Materials Group (1417)

_____ 6. Provides technical information and assistance to the Hazardous Materials Group and the Planning Section using various resources (1417)

_____ 7. Evaluates and prioritizes victims for treatment (1417)

A. Assistant Safety Officer

B. Decontamination Team Leader

C. Entry Team Leader

D. Hazardous Materials Branch Director/Group Supervisor

E. Safe Refuge Area Manager

F. Site Access Control Leader

G. Technical Specialist

Modes of Operation

Match the mode of operation listed with the correct description. Each choice will be used once.

_____ 1. Provides confinement of the hazard to a given area (1428)

_____ 2. Includes actions to actively control the hazard (1428)

_____ 3. Isolates the area to protect the public and emergency responders, but allows the incident to run its course on its own (1428)

A. Defensive

B. Nonintervention

C. Offensive

Control Zones

Match the control zone listed with the correct description. Each choice will be used once.

_______ 1. Area surrounding incident that is potentially very dangerous either because it presents a threat in the form of a hazardous material or the effects thereof (1468)

_______ 2. Area adjoining the hot zone and the cold zone (1468)

_______ 3. Used to carry out all logistical support functions of the incident (1467)

_______ 4. Area located in the warm zone where contaminated clothing, people, and equipment can be cleaned or secured (1467)

_______ 5. Area serving as a safe place to wait for evacuation and/or decontamination (1467)

_______ 6. Area(s) where personnel and equipment awaiting assignment to the incident are held to keep responders and equipment out of the way and safe until assigned (1467)

_______ 7. Safe location within cold zone where emergency personnel can rest, sit, or lie down, have food and drink, and have medical conditions evaluated (1467)

_______ 8. Area within the cold zone where injured victims and personnel can be medically assessed and treated (1467)

A. Area of safe refuge
B. Cold zone
C. Decontamination zone
D. Hot zone
E. Rehabilitation area
F. Staging area
G. Triage/treatment area
H. Warm zone

Multiple Choice

Write the correct answers on the blanks provided.

_____ 1. Which of the following is a responsibility ONLY an Operations-Level responder can perform? (1415)

A. Transmit information to an appropriate authority and call for assistance
B. Establish scene control by isolating the hazardous area and denying entry
C. Recognize the type of container at a site and identify the material in it if possible
D. Develop a defensive plan of action to address the problems presented by the incident

_____ 2. Which of the following is the FIRST life safety priority at a haz mat/WMD incident? (1415)

A. Safety of victims
B. Safety of emergency responders
C. Safety of those within 100 feet (30 m) of incident
D. Safety of those within 1 mile (1.6 km) of incident

_____ 3. Which of the following ensures control of a large-scale incident involving multiple agencies with overlapping authority and responsibility? (1418)

A. NIMS-ICS

B. Unified Command

C. National Response Framework

D. Multiagency incident action plan

_____ 4. Which of the following are a well-thought-out, organized course of events developed to address all phases of incident control within a specified time? (1428)

A. Strategic goal

B. Tactical objective

C. Mode of operation

D. Incident action plan

_____ 5. Which portions of the *ERG* list hazardous materials by name? (1433)

A. Blue pages

B. Green pages

C. Yellow pages

D. Orange pages

_____ 6. Which of the following is the distance within which all persons are considered for evacuation in all directions from the haz mat spill or leak source? (1434)

A. Hazard control zone

B. Initial isolation zone

C. Evacuation distances

D. Initial isolation distances

_____ 7. Which of the following statements regarding air-purifying respirators (APRs) is MOST accurate? (1445)

A. They protect against a host of contaminants.

B. They are recommended for use at all types of terrorist incidents.

C. They protect against materials that can be absorbed through the skin.

D. They include disposable filters, canisters, or cartridges on one or both sides of the facepiece.

_____ 8. Structural fire fighting protective clothing will provide adequate protection against: (1449)

A. projectiles and shrapnel.

B. extremely high temperatures.

C. all types of biological agents.

D. some types of radiological materials.

_____ 9. Which EPA level of protection is worn when the highest level of respiratory protection is necessary, but a lesser level of skin protection is needed? (1455)

A. Level A

B. Level B

C. Level C

D. Level D

_____ 10. Which of the following provides protection against liquid, solid, and/or vapor CB agents and radioactive alpha and beta particles? (1459)

A. Chemical-protective clothing

B. Mission-Oriented Protective Posture

C. Joint service lightweight integrated suit

D. Structural fire fighting protective clothing

_____ 11. Which of the following is the area(s) where personnel and equipment awaiting assignment are held? (1470)

A. Staging area

B. Area of safe refuge

C. Triage/treatment area

D. Decontamination area

_____ 12. In order to protect responders, what is the minimum number of backup members that must be standing by at an incident? (1473)

A. Two

B. Three

C. Four

D. Five

_____ 13. Which public protection method is an active (offensive) role or aggressive posture to physically protect those in harm's way? (1481)

A. Evacuation

B. Decontamination

C. Sheltering-in-place

D. Protecting/Defending-in-place

_____ 14. Which type of decontamination involves stripping contaminated individuals and washing them quickly? (1482)

A. Mass decontamination

B. Technical decontamination

C. Chemical decontamination

D. Emergency decontamination

_____ 15. Which spill control and confinement tactic is primarily used to control shallow liquid spills and often involves organic-based materials? (1489)

A. Dilution
B. Absorption
C. Adsorption
D. Blanketing/covering

_____ 16. Which spill control and confinement tactic can use available earthen materials or materials carried on response vehicles? (1490)

A. Dilution
B. Absorption
C. Vapor suppression
D. Dike, dam, diversion, and retention

_____ 17. Which spill control and confinement tactic is generally conducted by applying a fog stream to a breach in a container or directly onto a spill? (1492)

A. Dilution
B. Dissolution
C. Vapor dispersion
D. Vapor suppression

_____ 18. On high pressure tanks, emergency remote shutoff valves are located: (1494)

A. built into the valve box.
B. on the left front corner of the tank.
C. on the right front corner of the tank.
D. in the center of the tank near valves and piping.

_____ 19. Which of the following is a guideline for working at terrorist and criminal incidents? (1495)

A. Protect evidence at the crime scene
B. Place any suspects under arrest immediately
C. Put your protection above the needs of others
D. Contact contaminated surfaces only if absolutely necessary

_____ 20. Which of the following is performed to gather information from all operating personnel and includes a hazardous communication briefing? (1497)

A. Critique
B. On-scene debriefing
C. After action analysis
D. Operational recovery

Short Answer

Write the correct answers on the blanks provided.

1. List five factors that should be considered during initial size-up. (1423)

2. What should happen if an IAP is successful? (1430)

3. List six items to provide when calling an emergency response center. (1441-1442)

4. What can a response center do after gathering information? (1442)

5. What are the physical limitations of PPE? (1454)

6. List five ways to prevent heat exposure. (1461-1462)

7. What are five measures for protecting responders? (1471-1472)

8. What factors are related to large-scale evacuations? (1478-1479)

9. What are three guidelines for decontamination operations? (1484-1485)

10. What actions are performed during operational recovery? (1497)

Crossword Puzzle

Across

1. Overall plan for incident control established by the incident commander that involves protection of exposures, as opposed to aggressive, offensive intervention
5. Circular zone, with a radius equivalent to the initial isolation distance, within which persons may be exposed to dangerous concentrations upwind of the source and may be exposed to life-threatening concentrations downwind of the source
6. Overall plan for incident control established by the incident commander (IC) in which responders take aggressive, direct action on the material, container, or process equipment involved in an incident
7. Strategy for handling fires involving hazardous materials, in which the fire is allowed to burn until all of the fuel is consumed
14. Clothing designed to shield or isolate individuals from the chemical, physical, and biological hazards that may be encountered during operations involving hazardous materials
15. Downwind distance from a hazardous materials incident within which protective actions should be implemented
16. Written or unwritten plan for the disposition of an incident; contains the overall strategic goals, tactical objectives, and support requirements for a given operational period during an incident
17. Safe area outside of the warm zone where equipment and personnel are not expected to become contaminated and special protective clothing is not required; the incident command post and other support functions are typically located in this zone
18. Lowest level of training established by the National Fire Protection Association® for first responders at hazardous materials incidents

Down

2. The physical process of immediately reducing contamination of individuals in potentially life-threatening situations, with or without the formal establishment of a decontamination corridor
3. Document that provides guidance on how communities, states, the U.S. federal government, and private-sector and nongovernmental partners conduct all-hazards emergency response
4. Distance within which all persons are considered for evacuation in all directions from a hazardous materials incident
8. In the Incident Command System, a shared command role in which all agencies with geographical or functional responsibility establish a common set of incident objectives and strategies. In unified command there is a single incident command post and a single operations chief at any given time
9. Area between the hot and cold zones that usually contains the decontamination corridor; typically requires a lesser degree of personal protective equipment than the Hot Zone
10. U.S. regulations in Title 29 (Labor) CFR 1910.120 for cleanup operations involving hazardous substances and emergency response operations for releases of hazardous substances
11. Level of training established by the National Fire Protection Association® allowing first responders to take defensive actions at hazardous materials incidents
12. System used for sorting and classifying accident casualties to determine the priority for medical treatment and transportation
13. Potentially hazardous area immediately surrounding the incident site; requires appropriate protective clothing and equipment and other safety precautions for entry

1
2
3
4
5
6
7
8
9
10
11
12
13
14
15
16
17
18